# OWEN COON

## AND THE

# AMERICAN DREAM

*Richard Cahan*

CHICAGO
CITYFILES PRESS
LEGACY SERIES

Published by CityFiles Press, Chicago.
Produced and designed by Michael Williams.
Printed and bound by Friesens in Canada.

ISBN: 0-9785450-0-1

First edition of 1500.

# Contents of the Book

CHAPTER                                                          PAGE

Foreword . . . . . . . . . . VII

I.      The Perfect Prototype . . . . . . . 1
II.     Cars, Credit, and Crisis . . . . . . 23
III.    Sponsoring Dreams . . . . . . . 45
IV.     The Scholars . . . . . . . . . 65
V.      The War Changes Everything . . . . 85
VI.     Post-War Economics . . . . . . . 110
VII.    The Foundation . . . . . . . . 133

Afterword . . . . . . . . . . 159
Appendix . . . . . . . . . . 163
Acknowledgments . . . . . . . . 189

# Foreword

Owen L. Coon was a leader in the automobile finance industry from the time of its infancy in the mid-1920s until his untimely death in 1948 at age fifty-four. He was the force and genius behind General Finance Corporation, which came to be known to millions of people in the 1950s and 1960s as the firm of "Friendly Bob Adams."

Owen and his father saw a timely business opportunity in the area of automobile finance. Owen, through tireless work and with tremendous business acumen, built a hugely successful enterprise that enabled the average American to own an automobile and that helped make consumer credit a staple of American life. Owen himself became quite wealthy in the process. However, his purpose in making money was not so much self-enrichment, but rather to make his mark, to make his family secure, to remember those who had helped him, and to provide to others the same educational opportunities that he had received.

"The only thing that lasts is what one does for others," Owen once wrote. During his life, he implemented that philosophy of service in two principal ways. The first was through the Hardy Scholarships program, which he established at Northwestern University in 1935. The second was through his family foundation, which he created in 1946.

The Owen L. Coon Foundation has been managed during the past six decades by individuals who knew Owen personally and by the next generation of family members. The present board commissioned this biography principally so that future board members will be knowledgeable about the goals, ideals, and accomplishments of Owen L. Coon, and thereby more ably serve. While favorable, the book is not a eulogy. Owen Coon, like all of us, had his strengths and weaknesses.

Owen Coon often used the phrase "links in the chain." When doing so, he was referring to the transmission of values from his mentor, Professor Clarion DeWitt Hardy, through himself to future Hardy

Scholars. Clearly, however, that phrase is equally applicable to the successive generations of foundation board members and to the many people who have been touched by the foundation's good works over time.

We are grateful for the effort that author Richard Cahan has made in researching and writing this book. Foundation member and Associate Professor Kimberly Segall has also provided her perspective on the life of Owen Coon.

We dedicate this book to all Hardy Scholars—past, present, and future—and to all past directors of the Owen L. Coon Foundation.

RICHARD O. BRIGGS
PRESIDENT
OWEN L. COON FOUNDATION
CHICAGO, ILLINOIS
JUNE 1, 2006

# CHAPTER ONE

# The Perfect Prototype

---

"MY GRANDFATHER WAS EXCEEDINGLY POOR, AND
THE TALES OF HARDSHIP THAT MY FATHER AND HIS
FAMILY TELL OF THE EARLY DAYS OF THEIR STRUG-
GLE TO GET ON THEIR FEET ARE SOMETHING THAT I
SHALL NEVER FORGET."

The transformation of Owen L. Coon began in a Sunday school class during the early 1930s.

Owen was chosen to teach a group of sixth graders at the First United Methodist Church of Evanston. The assignment seemed perfect. As a major contributor to the church, just north of Chicago, and a leader of fund drives, Owen Coon was a pillar of the community. But Owen had misgivings. He took the pastor aside, admitted he went to church because it seemed "like the thing to do," and told the pastor that he did not believe all the Bible stories. The pastor listened, but asked Owen to give the children a try. "I had a wonderful, invigorating experience with them," Owen wrote in 1935. He read aloud several religious tracts, and soon came to realize that he was not "a probable atheist," as he called himself. One of the books he read was a children's Easter story that explained the difference between our body and our soul. The book, he wrote, taught him about immortality.

"If I take a candle and light it—rays of light shine forth," Owen wrote. "Those rays of light tear through space thousands of miles per second. They keep going on and on and on." Even if the candle is extinguished, the candle's light rays continue to spread. "And so it is with us," Owen wrote. "Our body is the flame, and our soul is the rays of light. The body, like the flame, finally dies out, but the rays of light, our spirit, can go on and on."

This is what defined Owen Coon's philosophy. And this is why Owen Coon's story is alive today, more than a half century after his death.

"When we speak of immortality, we mean our spirit—our influence, being relived in the lives of others that come after us," he wrote. "If we pass out good rays of light from our flame, that influence, that immortality of our spirit will carry on and on and be relived again and again in the lives of others yet to come." That Easter story reshaped Owen Coon. It inspired him to think deeply about the meaning of his life and the legacy he wished to create. "Prior to that time I ran my business without ethical principles," he wrote. "Such does not exist today."

It was with this thought in mind—the footsteps in the sand that one leaves behind—that Owen established a scholarship program at Northwestern University, his alma mater, in the name of Professor Clarion DeWitt Hardy, his mentor. "Such is my own personal solution to the much discussed question of immortality," Coon wrote to Hardy. "Our heaven, as I see it, is what we make it—and is lived on Earth in the lives of others."

Owen would write about immortality often. He wanted to use his money to make teachers of Hardy's caliber available to more and more students. The scholarships would aid in the "development of boys into men who will make their influence for good felt in turn upon others in a constantly widening circle," he wrote. "There and only there lies that intangible immortality for me."

Years later, well after the deaths of Owen Coon and Clarion Hardy, one of winners of those Hardy Scholarships gave a speech in honor of Coon. The speaker, James A. Rahl, had been granted free tuition in 1936 to attend Northwestern, and had gone on to become a lawyer. By 1961, he was a distinguished law professor at Northwestern. But he never forgot Owen. "Many of you knew him," Rahl noted in his speech. "For those of you who didn't, let me just say that he was a big man in every way—an extraordinary person—human, generous, and philosophical. He regarded his education as a great gift, not really something that he had earned so much as something others had provided for him, and he never lost this feeling of obligation to others who had helped him."

Owen believed that education made him a better person, and he was driven by a desire to pass along that opportunity to others. "He visualized this as a continuing process of each recipient, in turn, doing something for others," Rahl said. "Indeed, he described that as a form of immortality, and he used to charge the scholars themselves as being links in the chain, from Professor Hardy through him to the scholar, and then to future recipients through whatever their good works might be." These links have continued since Owen's death. The chain has continued through his family and through the foundation he created. This is the story of that chain.

‡    ‡    ‡    ‡

ON THE SURFACE, Owen Coon was the prototype of the successful twentieth century American businessman. Born in a small town, he came to the big city to make his first fortune. He lived in an English-style mansion in the suburbs, was driven downtown in a Cadillac coupe, talked on a Dictaphone, vacationed in Hot Springs and Mexico, corresponded on stationery that boasted his company's net worth, stayed at the Savoy, swore among his business associates, discussed debentures, smoked Webster Fancytails, joined a country club and owned a power boat. "While his close friends say he hasn't taken a drink in more than eight years, Owen Coon is not squeamish about those who find pleasure in an occasional highball or a cocktail," wrote *Fortune* magazine. And he had a dutiful wife who stayed at home, collected porcelain and hosted tea parties.

As a businessman, Owen was known for his fearlessness and extraordinary ability to adapt to changing times. Compact and solid, his confidence, intelligence, and innate efficiency gave him the look and feel of an entrepreneur from a Monopoly game. He opened a small automobile loan company that grew as America's car craze grew and helped shape the car culture that defines us today. He built a company that flourished during the Depression and shifted gears during World War II. When the war put an end to the production of automobiles and a near end to car loans, Owen remodeled his company into a conglomerate of industries, both aiding and profiting from the war effort.

Owen Coon's General Finance Corporation was renowned for helping middle-class American families use credit to purchase cars. "General Finance had an impact on consumers, particularly moderate-income families," said longtime company executive Emmett Harry Kitts. "The company helped open up the idea of who could borrow money. It was a pioneer in the consumer finance business."

In 1945, *Finance* magazine detailed how Owen built General Finance to a firm with a net worth of $7.2 million by the end of the war. Coon had an uncanny ability to figure his way through changing economic conditions, wrote the magazine. "He has a natural born talent for 'finding the answer.' He is a first-class salesman, with a persuasive personality, and a distinct flair for getting his point over." *Finance* contrasted Coon's accomplishments with his easy-going manner. "From his outward appearance, it is hard to associate such a quiet spoken, unpretentious individual as Owen Coon is with such a spectacular achievement," the magazine wrote. "In stature, he is average size. He does not have that commanding 'captain of industry' personality. But, on the mental gridiron, he has proved to the satisfaction of the bankers and business men in the Middle West that he would be entitled to an All-American rating." Owen, wrote *Finance*, possessed the spirit of an explorer because he was never afraid to figure out new paths.

While he was educated as a lawyer and devoted twenty years to finance and banking, Owen "has been knee deep in engineers, sales managers, accountants, tax experts, movie producers, and virtually every type of professional men," the magazine reported. "It is uncanny how he is able to speak their language, get their viewpoint, and size up a technical problem which would baffle the minds of many topflight engineers. But Owen Coon is at his best when he analyzes a financial statement. He has a genius for figures and the way that he has been able to put lame operations on a moneymaking basis is something to be marveled at."

Owen Coon is a significant figure in the history of American business because he exemplified how a man of skill can succeed in bad times. He played a large role in legitimizing finance companies and making credit a part of American life. He made the purchase of cars possible for many Americans, developed policies that streamlined borrowing, and created standards of upfront financial disclosure that benefit consumers to this day. "Owen's biggest contribution was the integrity he brought to finance companies," said his son, Harry H. Coon. "In the old day, banks would not finance automobiles. Bankers called them 'tin-can loans' and looked down their noses at that kind of financing." Owen led the fight to upgrade the image of finance companies and legitimize the concept of consumer borrowing.

To attract buyers, Owen played it straight with consumers. "A strong advocate of full and complete disclosure of finance charges, he has championed a vigorous, forward-looking campaign designed to improve the public relations of the finance companies with the American people," wrote one reporter. To get money, he also played it straight with bankers. "More than any one man, he was responsible for developing the auditing procedure that later came into general acceptance," *Finance* wrote. "He has always believed in putting all of his cards right out on the table top."

But like all us all, Owen struggled with everyday problems and family difficulties, some of his own making. Although known as a kindly benefactor, he stumbled badly in helping his first wife battle mental illness. A champion of education, he sadly watched as each of his children dropped out of college. Owen was known for his dreams, big dreams that he likely knew were not fully attainable. The scholarship program that he set up in 1935 was the first of many projects that Owen started to make the world a better place. He helped the handicapped by working to rejuvenate Goodwill Industries, and he valiantly attempted to reform the Protestant church, which he saw—with a businessman's eye—as financially inefficient and ineffective.

Typical of the business titans of his age, Owen was driven. He pursued fortune after fortune, determined to provide the best for his family and make his mark. He worked sixteen-hour days. "He is a man without any other hobby than business, but, in view of its great variety, it appears to be fun instead of travail," *Finance* wrote. "He appears sorry that each day has only twenty-four hours in which things can be accomplished." This, however, was the public man. Although he seldom said so, he harbored resentment at times that others had more time to spend at home. Once in a great while, he confided to business associates that he felt a burden daily.

More than fifty years since his death, Owen Coon is something of a mythical figure—especially to his grandchildren, who hardly knew him. His three children— Eleanor Briggs, Harry Coon, and Owen Coon Jr.—saw their father as a grand patriarch who had little time for them except during the holiday season. Somehow, however, he transmitted his love and his values to them. His children honor him today by keeping his foundation vital and active. They honor him by keeping his name and dream alive. He would be proud of them. And they honor him by passing down his stories and ideals to their children and grandchildren.

The number of people who personally knew Owen is dwindling. But the number of people who have been helped by his largesse continues to grow. Each year, more Northwestern University students take their place in the chain that Owen began. "One man's life touches so many others," angel-to-be Clarence Oddbody tells George Bailey in the film *It's A Wonderful Life*. "When he's not there it leaves an awfully big hole." This book will look at the man with many dreams. It will follow Owen Coon down a long road, one littered with failed businesses, a tragic marriage, and a career that left little time for a personal life. But it's a road that also led to remarkable business success and a proud legacy—Owen Coon is still making the world a bit better.

‡ ‡ ‡ ‡

WE ARE SHAPED by our families. The wise, hardworking, and lucky among us go on, in turn, to influence the world beyond our family home. So it was with Owen Coon. He was born into a family formed by tradition, ambition, and the vigorous Midwest. All were evident at the event that launched his parents' life together—their wedding.

The marriage drew lots of local attention. More than 100 relatives and guests gathered at the home of Mr. and Mrs. Lewis A. Rike in the central Illinois town of LeRoy on April 7, 1892, to attend the union of their daughter, Rose O. Rike, to James Samuel Coon. The wedding was a celebration of success and potential, for the Rikes ran a profitable orchard at the edge of town. Moreover, young James was an up-and-coming cashier at the First National Bank of LeRoy. One reporter commented that this was "one of those popular weddings, which take place only once in a great while."

The wedding was full of finery and lace, drawing the regard of the local press. Rose (born December 16, 1872, in LeRoy) and James (born May 1, 1866, in the town of Higginsville near Rantoul) were "well known and highly respected in the social and church circles of LeRoy," according to the *LeRoy Journal*. A reporter from Rantoul agreed, writing: "Last night at LeRoy occurred one of the most notable matrimonial events that has taken place in that city for a considerable length of time." To the strains of Mendelssohn's Wedding March, which Miss Maude Kellar played on the piano, the Reverend J. M. West led the bridal pair through the parlor, where they paused to stand beneath a fragrant marriage bell of carnations and heliotrope. "To the right and to the left, the most lovely, full-bloomed lilies added their splendid signifi-

6

cance to the scene," the *Journal* reporter wrote. Each detail suggested a certain country elegance and affluence: "The bride appeared in a rich and elegant costume of albatross and crepe de chine, bearing in her left hand a primrose bouquet of richest hue, sweetest odor."

The groom, wrote the *Journal*, was dressed in a "superb Prince Albert costume of faultless black, and was certainly happy with his immediate surroundings and future prospects." James, born and raised about forty-five miles to the east in Rantoul, had moved to LeRoy several years previously, first working for the *Journal* and then at the bank. He made his mark in town by building a small house, which still stands, to woo his future bride.

The two reporters, from LeRoy and Rantoul, noted that the wedding, as joyful and perfect as it was, did not measure up to the celebration. "Then came the social and nuptial repast, and our pencil is far too dull to do justice to this part of the program," the *Journal* reporter wrote. "It was grandly sumptuous, and was served and enjoyed to the full capacity of each guest. The newly wedded pair were the recipients of a large number of valuable and useful presents, and will soon be snugly housed in their neat new cottage, and remain among our permanent citizens."

James Coon's roots were ground deep in eighteenth century America. Abner Sutton Coon, his grandfather, was born on April 29, 1794, in Geneva, New York. A Pennsylvania Dutchman, he met and married Lydia Pope on September 19, 1818, in New Jersey. Lydia, who was born in Germany on September 10, 1796, moved with her new husband to New York state and later to Hanover Township in Ohio, about forty miles east of Columbus in Licking County. Both Abner, who died on June 13, 1844, and Lydia, who died May 4, 1851, were buried in Hanover Cemetery near Newark, Ohio.

The ambition and drive that marked this booming era in America spurred the Coons westward. Abner worked as a farmer and shoemaker; Lydia as a weaver. They had five boys and four girls, born from 1819 to 1838. The children—Israel, David, Sally Ann, Eliza, Mary, Charlotte, John, George, and Samuel—reflected the times and the place where they were born. They were upright, serious, and productive members of Midwestern small towns. Several died young, but the others moved farther West, set on finding land and opportunity on the frontier. At least eight of Abner and Lydia's grandchildren became farmers. Two became grocers and two owned grain elevators. Others labored as carriage makers, cigar makers, manufacturers, attorneys, wood workers, carpet salesmen, patrolmen, insurance clerks, stenographers, and bakers. The early Coons stayed connected as an extended family, holding family reunions as late as the early twentieth century.

All of Abner and Lydia's children patterned their days to the ongoing cycles of small town life. Second-born David became a Deedsville, Indiana, farmer. Dressed in black formal clothes, he kept his hair parted down the middle and his gray beard strictly beneath his chin. In photographs, he and his wife, Sarah Catherine Drumm, have the no-nonsense look of Grant Wood subjects. Sixth-born Charlotte moved west to Illinois after marrying John Little, a downstate Rantoul farmer. Eighth-born George manufactured carriages in Zanesville, Ohio.

Samuel, who would become Owen's grandfather, was Abner and Lydia's youngest child. He was born on February 18, 1838, moved west to Rantoul, and married Mary Jane Collison on November 21, 1861. (The Collison family helped establish the East Central Illinois town of Collison.) Samuel and Mary Jane had three boys and two girls, including James Samuel Coon, Owen's father, born in Collison, about twenty-five miles east of Rantoul. Owen's father attended public schools in Rantoul and graduated in 1884, one of only two members of Rantoul High School's third class. Early life was not easy for James, according to his granddaughter Eleanor Briggs, because his father, Samuel, was an alcoholic who lost much of the family's wealth. "James wore paper in his shoes, and never got over it," she said. "He was determined to avoid liquor and to make money."

Owen wrote little about his ancestors, but in 1944 he gave Northwestern University money to start a scholarship program for Rantoul students to honor his family's hard work. "My grandfather came there before the railroad was even put through," he said. "My grandfather was exceedingly poor, and the tales of hardship that my father and his family tell of the early days of their struggle to get on their feet are something that I shall never forget."

On the other side of the family tree, Rose Rike's family came to America in the 1700s. Her great-great grandfather, Heinrich Reich, left Germany with his wife, Margaret Shuck. "I was always told that we were descendants of serfs from Frankfurt," said Eleanor Briggs. "They won their freedom for eighteen gilders." The names of Heinrich and

Margaret are still listed in a German-language family Bible, along with a permit allowing them to emigrate. They were upstanding citizens, according to the permit.

It is unclear exactly when the Reichs left Germany. "In the year of Christ 1778, the 29 April is born Jacob Reich in the evening at nine o'clock," according to records found in the family Bible. Jacob Reich, Rose's great-grandfather, apparently was born in Germany and probably emigrated to Frederick County, Maryland, with his family, which chose the more American last name of Rike. Jacob Rike married Catherine Crumbaugh, born in 1786, in Maryland. The couple moved in 1812 to Montgomery County, Ohio, where they ran a dry-good store and a river ferry. Jacob and Catherine moved to LeRoy in 1859. Jacob died in 1864 and Catherine died in 1878.

The Rikes had five children, including Mordecai Henry Rike, Rose's grandfather, who was born on March 5, 1816, near Dayton, Ohio. He married Mary Ann Ewry in 1838, and they also had five children, including Lewis Augustus Rike, Rose's father. Lewis was born in Beavertown, near Dayton, on August 14, 1841. Mordecai and the family moved to LeRoy in 1857. He and Lewis scouted the land on a buggy and the family moved by train. Mordecai suffered a stroke in 1865, and was primarily confined to his home for decades. He died in 1892. Lewis Rike apparently ran away from home to enlist in the Union Army at nearby Springfield near the end of the Civil War. He was a part of the Yates Phalanx, a regiment named in honor of Illinois Governor Richard Yates. Although he was still in training at the end of the war, Lewis felt a lifelong pride in his connection to the Grand Army of the Republic.

Living in LeRoy, Lewis drove a stagecoach between LeRoy and Bloomington, about fifteen miles to the northwest. After his marriage to Leah Melissa Long, he went into the nursery and florist business. "He was very successful financially and leaves his family a goodly heritage of this world's goods," his 1908 obituary noted.

Leah Melissa Long Rike was the daughter of Midwest pioneers Henry and Sarah Ann Long. Leah was born in 1848 in Lebanon, Ohio, and moved in a covered wagon to a farm four miles west of LeRoy in 1853. The family built a home there, where she lived most of her married life. She and Lewis taught Sunday school at Methodist Episcopal Church. Writing about herself, Leah stated: "She was a faithful attendant at prayer meeting—seldom ever missed during the stormiest weather—her greatest love and desire during her Christian life was the saving of souls." Lewis and Leah had three children, including Rose Rike, Owen's mother.

In many ways, Leah lived a double life. She wrote fiction under the pen name Elizabeth Irving. Her novel, *A New World*, was printed by M.A. Donohue & Company in 1905. Wrote the local paper: "She has a reputation outside of her own community as a brilliant writer and has written for magazines and newspapers for years." She also published a book called *Child Training*. In a reflection on her early LeRoy childhood, Leah offered details of her rural childhood, viewing her country town—just the sort of world young Owen would know—through a lens of nostalgia. She wrote:

> Who is there of us who does not read with pleasure of those far off days that we spent in the little red school house by the roadside? What a peculiar fascination lingers around the dingy room with its warped floors, its battered seats covered with initials carved by some boys with a Jack-knife?

Leah died in 1943, at age ninety-six, one of LeRoy's oldest residents. Owen and his brother, Byron, served as pallbearers at their grandmother's funeral.

‡    ‡    ‡    ‡

AFTER THEIR FAIRYTALE WEDDING, James Coon and Rose Rike encountered rough economic times. James was an excellent worker. He ran a pony cart delivering vegetables as a boy, then worked for the *LeRoy Journal* and the First National Bank of LeRoy. After the 1892 wedding, James worked sorting mail on the Pumpkin Vine railroad line that linked Rantoul and LeRoy. But the job was short lived. One day he headed home with his belongings on a stick, slung over his shoulder. "Rose," he announced, "we need to get back to Rantoul so I can get a job." James and his brother, Edmond, soon started an assortment of businesses in Rantoul, a town 110 miles south of Chicago. They bought several grain elevators and built a huge icehouse that could produce up to 700 tons of ice for home refrigeration. After that, they built the Coon Brothers Telephone Exchange. When that business burned to the ground, along with most of the Rantoul business district, in a devastating 1901 fire, the Coons quickly rebuilt. They strung telephone wires throughout Rantoul and soon established the first independent telephone exchange in East Central Illinois, connecting Rantoul's neighbor to the east, Potomac, to Rantoul's neighbor to the west, Fisher. The following year, the company offered long-distance service, a major event. "Coon Brothers Telephone Company has consolidated with the Central Union Company so that their subscribers can talk to any place in the United States over their lines by paying the usual toll rate," the *Rantoul Press* reported. The telephone exchange, later sold and renamed the Rantoul Telephone Company, earned the brothers a great deal of money, which they invested in farms.

James and Rose's first son, Owen Lewis Coon, was born on July 1, 1894, in a two-story, Victorian house in Rantoul. It was one of those eye-catching houses with a wraparound porch and fancy railing on Bell Avenue. Owen arrived during the first years of James' business successes. Byron Samuel Coon, the couple's second son, was born on April 2, 1903, after James had more fully established himself. Rose tended to the home, looked after the children, and played the organ.

In the fall of 1901, the Coon brothers donated a rural home they had purchased in nearby Mink Grove to help start the Children's Home in Rantoul. It was Owen's first taste of philanthropy. The house provided shelter for about fifteen children, who usually stayed a few months before being adopted. The Rantoul Children's Home operated there until 1908, when it moved to a modern facility. The Coons's house reverted back to the brothers, who kept it for public events and an annual Coon Family Reunion.

In 1903, James Coon moved his family back to LeRoy, where he served as the president of the First National Bank of LeRoy. The family apparently remained in LeRoy for another two or three years. Owen's 1902-03 third grade report card was from the Rantoul Schools. His fourth grade and fifth grade report cards were from the LeRoy Public Schools. Photos taken when he was in sixth grade show him back at Rantoul.

But LeRoy continued to hold a special place in Rose Coon's heart. And the Coons occupied a special place in the town's memory. Owen's accomplishments often were chronicled in the *LeRoy Journal*. In 1945, almost forty years after the Coons left LeRoy, the *Journal* reprinted the long *Finance* magazine article about Owen's career. Rose Coon, then seventy-two, wrote a note of thanks from her apartment at the Orrington Hotel in Evanston. "I received the *LeRoy Journal* this eve and imagine my surprise to see that my boy was honored by front page news in my hometown paper. I cannot tell you how I appreciate the same. Many, many thanks for your kindness. ...LeRoy has always been very dear to me. I spent many happy years there. I shall never forget."

‡    ‡    ‡    ‡

By the end of grammar school, Owen had established himself as a good student. He ranked near the top of his class in eighth grade, and his teacher wrote: "Work excellent. Noticeable improvement in writing. Other work excellent." He continued to excel at Rantoul High School. One explanation for Owen's academic success may have been his parents' formidable expectations. James and Rose were not typical turn-of-the-century Rantoul residents. James was a high achiever, and both he and Rose saw the value in a good education and broad experiences. In July 1909, after his freshman year at Rantoul High, Rose took Owen on a grand tour of Europe. They traveled to London, Glasgow, Paris, Brussels, Amsterdam, Cologne, Lucerne, Lugano, Venice, Rome, and the Vatican. "More than anything else, she loved to travel," Eleanor Briggs recalled of Rose, "and my father stayed right up with her. They didn't miss a church." For a boy from little Rantoul, such a trip must have made a huge impression. For the rest of his life, he held on to a July 4, 1909, Red Star Line menu from the SS *Manitou*, hotel envelopes, railroad passes, and luggage tags.

At Rantoul High, Owen ran on the school track team and took part in the Rantoul Literary Society. In his senior year, he participated on the debate team. Taking the affirmative side on the question, "Resolved, That the initiative and referendum should be in every state," he wrote: "This will offer the public a chance to learn much about this obscure subject, and also permit the students of the high schools to broaden their political views of a republic."

By the end of his senior year, Owen was very much the leader of his class. He was in charge of raising money for the class memorial, a drinking fountain, and gave an address on Arbor Day after the school planted a three-year-old pine tree just south of the school sundial.

In the spring of 1912, the town of Rantoul lavished attention on its graduating high school class. Owen's parents hosted the annual reception for the senior class, faculty and board of trustees at their home. The rooms were decorated in the purple-and-white class colors and the purple-and-gold high school colors. Veal sandwiches, Saratoga chips, el doradoes, cake, and coffee were on the menu. "Soon the joyous party broke up, to meet no more as a whole," the local paper wrote. On May 14, 1912, the high school's first Maypole dance was held. A crowd estimated at between 600 and 1,000 townspeople came to watch the pole being wrapped and unwrapped in braids. "The first number was the seniors' farewell," a reporter wrote. "All persons taking part in the Maypole marched up, and around the pole, then all but the seniors took their places. Then the seniors marched around the pole several times and then off the field, all of the while singing the new song, 'R.H.S. Loyalty.' Great enthusiasm was expressed by all."

The following day, the senior class picnic was held. "Come in the morning—stay all day—and be a High School student again," the local paper declared. A team of freshmen and seniors took on the sophomores and juniors in baseball and then the seniors took on the alumni. The nineteen graduating seniors followed that with a hayride to Gordon's Grove near Penfield, about twelve miles east of Rantoul. "Supper was served at three p.m., after which the party departed for home in the rain, after one of the most gratifying times they had ever had in their lives, and arrived at Rantoul at 7:30, soaked and tired, but safe at last, and happy."

On May 30, Owen took part in the Class of 1912 play at the Neal Opera House in town. He starred as Colonel McMillen in *A Kentucky Belle*. Wrote the paper: "There was not a single hitch in the performance, and the encores were hearty and frequent." The opera house was filled to capacity two weeks later for the commencement of Rantoul High School. The Danville Quartet couldn't make it because one of its members was sick, so a trio of women from the Bloomington Conservatory of Music sang along with the Rantoul Orchestra. Owen Coon was valedictorian. He delivered a speech entitled "The Will as an Element of Success." Critiqued the paper: "The address was well written and well delivered."

This was a fine class, according to Rantoul Superintendent E. H. Miller, who also taught at the school. Not one of these students had been arrested or even been accused of a crime, he wrote in the local paper. Ninety-five percent of the city's grade school graduates had gone on to high school and eighty percent had made it to graduation, he wrote.

Fifteen percent of the class planned to go to college. Owen, the paper wrote, planned eventually to attend law school.

What a beautiful rural tableau these graduation days created. The senior class serenaded Miller the night before graduation. "A lovely table was presented by the class to their instructor," the paper reported. "School songs and different yells were given. The matter came as a surprise to the professor. A good time was enjoyed by all." When the final ceremony concluded, melancholy filled the air. Even the local reporters felt heavy-hearted. "One more school year with its frills and fusses, and with its trials and scraps, is over," the *Rantoul Press* reported. "Farewell to the class of 1912!"

‡     ‡     ‡     ‡

JAMES AND ROSE COON used the money they made in Rantoul to send Owen to Northwestern University—and that, they would always believe, changed the course of the family's life. "They all said, 'We'd all be down on the farm if it wasn't for Northwestern,'" Eleanor Briggs said. "I was lectured that often."

With the support of his family and the Rantoul community behind him, Owen Coon moved on to the next phase of his young life. His goals were clear. He entered the College of Liberal Arts at Northwestern as a member of the Class of 1916 with eighteen classroom credits. His application was straightforward. He was asked, "Of what church are you a member?" He answered, "The Methodist Church." He was asked: "What are your plans after graduation?" He answered: "Becoming a lawyer."

Owen thrived in the placid lakeside community of Evanston, Illinois. His was a focused approach to college for he knew he was primarily there for the academic courses and training. But he also busied himself in extracurricular activities. He served as the president of the Men's Literary Society and participated in theater and debate. He was initiated into the Aleph Tath Nun fraternity for good citizenship. During his first year, Owen volunteered at the Northwestern University Student Settlement Association, a house at 1400 West Augusta Boulevard on the city's Northwest Side established to assist the underprivileged. In 1913, he joined the First United Methodist Church of Evanston. In the next thirty-five years, he saw the church grow from about 900 members to

2,500, primarily thanks to the church's pastor, Dr. Ernest F. Tittle, who became a close friend.

Souvenirs from the plays and athletic events Owen attended while at Northwestern hint of good times: A smoker on October 4, 1912; a YMCA Stag on September 24, 1913; the University Circus on January 17, 1914. One newspaper clipping, saved from his sophomore year, was entitled: "Hurl Freshies Into Lake: Fifty Northwestern Sophomores Catch Youngsters Posting Warnings and Give Them a Chilly Bath." The clip reports that fifty sophomores in Owen's class tossed fifty freshmen into Lake Michigan after freshmen posted a warning that read: "To the lunkheaded sophomores: We, the class of 1917, hereby warn you yellow backed, evil thinking 1916 fish of the grand approach of the mighty army of 1917." Three months later, the freshmen got revenge by attacking the sophomore dinner at the Mission Tea Room in the Chicago neighborhood of Edgewater. The *Chicago Tribune* reported, "Owen Coon and Reginald Wright, down on the program as speakers at the banquet, were captured and tied to a boiler in the basement of the Sigma Alpha Epsilon fraternity house, but upper classmen who are members of that 'frat' ordered their release on condition that they would report to the freshmen again this evening before the banquet."

In his usual enthusiastic style, Owen happily threw in with his classmates and joined their cheers against the other classes. The class crowed:

> Nineteen sixteen the best class ever seen
> Around the world our boast is hurled,
> We have, we have no peers,
> For we're the true blue of the N and the U,
> Our like 'tis plain will cease again,
> For a hundred years.

Ironically, as it happened, Owen graduated from Northwestern at the end of his third year, on June 9, 1915, making him a member of the Class of 1915. He was able to complete his studies in just three years because he had begun college with college-level credits in hand and took heavy course loads.

Owen was on the honor roll during his first two years. In his first semester, he received an A in elocution, Latin, and mathematics; a

B in German, and a C in English. In his second semester, he received an A in German, Latin, and mathematics, and a B in English and elocution. In the first semester of his second year, he received an A in chemistry, English, history, public speaking, and debate, and a C in economics. In the second semester that year, he received an A in chemistry, English, history, public speaking, and a B in economics and psychology.

During the summer of 1914, Owen took three courses in political economics at the University of Wisconsin. Returning to Northwestern for his final undergraduate year, he received an A in two economics courses, history, public speaking, and debate, and got a B in philosophy.

Much of Northwestern's present Evanston campus was new during the years when Owen was a student there. Swift Hall opened in 1909, the Patten Gymnasium in 1910 and Harris Hall in 1915. About 1,000 undergraduates were enrolled on the Evanston campus when Owen was an undergraduate, and tuition was about $50 per semester. From his first year on campus, Owen was active in a new fraternity, a writing group known as the Scribblers. Owen took part in the Scribblers' campaign to construct a house on the Northwestern campus and was one of the first residents of the house, built for $35,000 and dedicated in 1914 on the university's North Quadrangle. Owen saved photos of the Scribblers during his three years as an undergraduate—photos showing the Scribblers' initiation, favorite professors, and something called the Dope Rush in 1913-14. He kept the Scribblers' initiation menu from a banquet at the Hotel LaSalle in December 1913 ("The great social event of the first semester," he wrote.), and saved photos showing him wearing a deep circular collar called a Marley. He also saved curious mentions of himself in Scribblers publications. In the summer of 1913, the group's newsletter noted a strange (and obviously offensive) name for Owen, "Nig Coon." The newsletter reported that he was running a gas plant in Rantoul as a summer job. In his second year, the newsletter compared Owen to the greatest of Greek orators when it reported: "Owen L. Coon, the Demosthenes of Rantoul (who ever heard of it before?), can shoot more hot air than anyone we know of at the present time. On cold mornings his hot air warms the house."

In addition to writing, Owen showed an interest in acting. He was a leading member of the freshman frolic, a musical production called *The Purple Princess*, staged at the Ravinia Theater in nearby Highland Park on May 10, 1913. He later joined Northwestern's Campus Players, winning the elected position of treasurer by student vote, despite the fact that the *Daily Northwestern* student newspaper accidentally omitted his name from the list of candidates. But Owen's shining moment onstage was in his final year when he played Elder Daniels in the first amateur production of George Bernard Shaw's *The Showing-Up of Blanco Posnet.* The student newspaper called it "the dramatic feature of the year at Northwestern."

The activity that would have the greatest influence on Owen was the Northwestern debate team. About twenty-five freshmen signed up for the team in Owen's first year. Coon made the cut, along with Irvin Fathschild and Karl Olson. "More spirit, both in numbers and in preparation, was shown by this year's participants than has been evidenced for some time," the *Daily Northwestern* reported. "In view of the fact that in this group are many men who have had experience in high school debating gives additional confidence to those who believe that the Northwestern freshmen will be able to defeat Chicago as they have for the last two years."

Back home in Rantoul, the local paper reported: "This is quite an honor for Owen and at once places him in an elevated position in his chosen college. To gain such signal honors in his first year is indeed noteworthy and a source of gratification to his parents and friends in Rantoul." The major event for the freshman team was the April 1913 debate against the University of Chicago at Annie May Swift Hall in Evanston. The team worked with coaches James Lawrence Lardner, an elocution instructor, and Clarion Hardy, a public speaking instructor, preparing to debate the question "Resolved, That college conference baseball players should be permitted to play summer baseball for pay without forfeiting their eligibility." Owen and the Northwestern Wildcats took the negative side and won the match.

Owen was promoted to the varsity team in his second year. The team's big match was against the University of Michigan in January 1914 at Ann Arbor. The team, accompanied by Coach Hardy, was composed of Owen, fellow sophomore Irvin Fathschild and junior Adolph Wickman. They faced the best of Michigan's law school in a debate in which Owen took the negative position to the question "Resolved, That the states should establish a schedule of minimum wages for unskilled labor, constitutionality conceded." Northwestern students were primed for the showdown. "Yesterday's chapel exercises, which were devoted to the two debating teams, rivaled those which usually precede a critical football game," the *Daily Northwestern* wrote. "The teams were given seats of honor on the platform and speeches were given by faculty members, members of former Northwestern debating teams and by representatives of the present squad."

In another article, a Northwestern reporter wrote: "Debaters don't get into the limelight very much. They work for a couple of months in the quiet of their rooms and finally emerge with fifteen minutes of oratory and facts on a weighty question and try to convince the public how this or that should be done. It is all very good, too. The training they receive is excellent, and the knowledge, which they hand out in nice capsule forms, is easily digested by their hearers. Then, if they make good, they have their path to Congress blazed a little clearer." The debate against Michigan was grueling, but the Northwestern varsity prevailed. It was the first time Michigan had been defeated on its home floor in thirteen years. "So unexpected was the victory that when the news reached Evanston from Ann Arbor all the dormitory students were aroused to celebrate the victory," the Northwestern paper reported. The *LeRoy Journal* allowed that Owen, "a former LeRoy boy," was instrumental in the victory. "Two of the judges declared that it was the best and most thoroughly prepared debate that they had ever heard."

Both Northwestern's negative and affirmative teams won the event. The Northwestern paper proclaimed: "Purple Debaters Win Great Double Victory: Affirmative Gets Unanimous Decision—Negative Result, 2 to 1." After the victory, the triumphant Owen sent a telegram with a religious tinge to his father. "Michigan stands beaten by Northwestern tonight," he wrote. "Vote two to one. First time in years Michigan has been defeated on home floor. They had all law school men. We had two sophomores of liberal arts. Particulars will follow. Not through ourselves but through Him we conquered." Owen was awarded a Gage Prize for excellence in debate by the university at the conclusion of the year.

Owen again made the varsity team in his third and final year as an undergraduate and again won the Gage Prize. His team lost, by a 2-1 vote, to the University of Chicago on Chicago's Hyde Park campus, but he performed well. Owen was on the negative side of the topic "Resolved, That the Monroe Doctrine should be abandoned as an American foreign policy," which meant that he was speaking in favor of the doctrine. "The question is a popular one," he wrote, "and doubly interesting at the present time, because of recent European developments." The *Daily Northwestern* reported: "Wickman, [Arthur] Burch, and Coon put up a splendid argument in defense of the doctrine, maintaining that it was in accordance with public policy, justified by international law and the practice of nations, and fundamental to the peace and safety of the United States." Owen would use the skills that he learned in debate throughout his professional life.

"Professor Hardy taught me to think straight," Owen wrote when he proposed the Hardy Scholarships. "It was the greatest single contribution to my education. I now realize the full nature of the obligation I owe and am taking this method to repay in part the benefit that I have received." But Hardy's lessons to Owen went well beyond how to debate. "I know that what I got from you was obtained not in the classroom, but in the hours at your home or in debate practice (just the four of us) in the room on the third floor of Annie May Swift Hall," he wrote Hardy during the 1930s. "As I look back on it, it was in those years that you got your licks on me, consciously or unconsciously. In other words, there came to exist a very personal relationship."

Years later, Owen reiterated his conviction that Hardy's influences on him and other students were life lessons. "By constant association with his students, singly and in groups, in his office—his home—and in walks on the campus, he taught them as much outside the class as within. He left the imprint of his personality, his thinking upon the minds and lives of scores of students."

Professor Hardy, Owen believed, taught his students five significant lessons:

> 1. To solicit criticism of one's thinking and acting, and accept it impartially without malice. "Such," Hardy would say, "is the only way one can always be certain to continue an education throughout life."
>
> 2. Learn to think straight. "Think straight," he would say.
>
> 3. "Never stand up to speak before an audience unless you have something to say—sit down when you have said it—and never stand up to say it if you must read it."

4. "Any problem can be solved if one has sufficient determination."

5. "The only thing that lasts is what one does for others."

Owen took these dictums to heart, and made decisions through-out the rest of his life based Hardy's principles. It's easy to see why Owen was so pleased and nostalgic about his Northwestern years. The academic and extracurricular success he experienced in high school con-tinued at the Evanston university. But it wasn't all fun. During summer breaks from college, Owen worked and played hard. He worked the farm, went to summer school, and traveled during his college years. In 1913, the Rantoul paper reported that Owen possessed "the finest stand of beans that ever was seen on full forty acres," on a farm near Rantoul. After another summer, a college paper jocularly reported, "Owen Coon returned the 20th from a few weeks sojourn in his home in Rantoul, Illi-nois, and 'Somewhere in Cupiddom' (wherever that accomplished young lady who was out here last year is)." During the summer break after his sophomore year, he went to school in Madison, Wisconsin, and one sum-mer he traveled West, touring Yellowstone National Park in Wyoming and the Cave of the Winds in Colorado.

Owen won eight major prizes in public speaking and debating and several academic honors during his three years as an undergraduate at Northwestern. He was elected to Delta Sigma Rho, an honorary debating society, and to Phi Beta Kappa, the nation's most prestigious undergraduate honors organization. He was a commencement speaker at graduation, on June 9, 1915, addressing his classmates on the topic, "The College Man in Political Reform."

No sooner did Owen have his undergraduate diploma in hand than he entered Northwestern University Law School, which was housed in the former Tremont House on the southeast corner of Lake and Dearborn streets in downtown Chicago. The school, with about 350 students, was under the control of John Henry Wigmore, one of the nation's preeminent experts in the law of evidence. Wigmore was dean from 1901 to 1929. Owen flew through high school and college, but struggled in law school, taking four years to finish. In part, it was the times—he took off a full year in an attempt to serve in the Great War.

And in part, it was his unbridled enthusiasm. Owen continued debating and worked as the liberal arts editor of the *Syllabus*, the student yearbook. The salute given to Owen by his friends in the *Syllabus* reads, "With all his faults we love him still. The stiller the better."

Owen chose courses that reflected his longtime interests in business and tax law. He took two prescribed reading courses, analytical jurisprudence, conflict of laws, Illinois law, legal ethics, federal tax, partnership, and surety classes. Owen was elected to the Order of the Coif, the law school honor society, and tied for first honors in scholarship. "It has been the custom to give only one award," the *Chicago Tribune* wrote in 1919, "but the faculty was unable to decide between the leaders." He shared the award with Marguerite Raeder.

But it was also in law school that Owen suffered his first academic setback. He wrote a thesis in support of a Master of Law degree, but his paper was not accepted. In those days, law school graduates received a Bachelor of Law degree upon graduation unless they did extra academic work. The ninety-two-page dissertation, on the topic of disputed claims in real estate purchases, was rejected by Wigmore, who curtly wrote: "Moved that the thesis submitted by Owen L. Coon, in its present form, is not found sufficient to warrant recommendation at this time for the degree of Master of Arts." Owen never revised the paper.

As hostilities in Europe drew the world's attention, Owen tried to enlist in the Marine Corps, but failed to pass the physical. He suffered from a breathing ailment that reduced his stamina. Determined to do his part, he obtained a leave from law school for the 1917-18 school year to perform "agricultural services" for the war effort, thinking this would also increase his stamina. He took charge of a farm in Two Buttes, Colorado, on land owned by his father and uncle. He wrote to Dean Wigmore that he farmed 220 acres of irrigated land, 140 acres of which was previously covered in buffalo grass and uncultivated. That summer, he said, he produced 240 tons of alfalfa hay, 500 bushels of maize and 16,000 pounds of beans, and placed in cultivation 120 acres of fall or winter wheat. Owen later told his daughter how he made certain to make the most of the water that trickled down to his farm from the Colorado highlands. "The water came in a ditch so he would sleep with his feet in the neighbor's ditch," Eleanor Briggs said. "Then when the water was in the neighbor's field, he would wake up and push the lever to water his field."

Owen studied for the Illinois bar exam while working on the farm. He passed the bar in 1918, after returning to Chicago to finish law school. That same year, he accepted enlistment in the Navy. He remained committed to serving in the war, but by the fall of 1918 the conflict was winding down and the fighting officially stopped on November 11, Armistice Day. However briefly, he carried the rank of ensign.

On May 22, 1918, Owen married Alice Elizabeth Wright, a fellow Northwestern student who received her diploma from the School of Oratory in 1917. Alice, born on June 8, 1896, in downstate Manteno, was the daughter of Elizabeth Seeger and George Wright. Like his father, Owen met his wife in church. "Byron said she wore a see-through filmy thing," said Eleanor Briggs. "And that was it."

# CHAPTER TWO

# Cars, Credit, and Crisis

"MY GRANDFATHER SAID, 'LET'S GO DOWN AND SEE
HOW HE DID IT.' THE MAN WAS LOANING MONEY
ON CARS. MY GRANDFATHER SAID, 'IF HE CAN DO
IT, WE CAN DO IT.' AND UP OVER THE BOILER ROOM
IN THAT OLD BENSON AVENUE GARAGE—I REMEMBER
IT—GRANDPA AND DAD STARTED THEIR BUSINESS."

During the decade leading to the Depression, Owen Coon established
a law practice, developed a cab company, and ran a finance company—a diversified portfolio for difficult times. Owen only practiced law
from 1919 to 1924, but it was as a lawyer that he won his first fortune.
"His law office began—and almost ended—in a small office in the YMCA
building on Chicago's LaSalle Street," wrote a reporter years later. Owen's
first months were difficult, and without financial success. He wrote his
father later, "Chicago was no place for a struggling lawyer."

James Coon may have felt sympathy for his son, but he didn't
show it. Instead, he came up with an idea that would change their lives.
James still owned grain elevators in the Rantoul area, and he was struck
by the fact that railroads seldom accepted responsibility for damage
caused to the grain they shipped. Small farmers everywhere had claims
against the huge carriers, James wrote his son, but farmers considered
themselves too weak to take the railroads to court. James suggested that
Owen start filing lawsuits against the railroads to win back damages
suffered by the farmers. Owen's father was determined to help his son
succeed. "Enclosed you will find my own batch," he wrote, wryly adding
that once Owen had begun collecting on some claims he could repay his
father for his law school expenses.

After winning one lawsuit for his father, Owen followed up with
a dozen or more lawsuits in his father's name against the railroads. The

cases, filed in the Municipal Court of Chicago, were similar in issues and language. Take, for example, the case of James S. Coon v. Chicago, Rock Island & Pacific Railway Company. Filed December 1, 1922, by attorney Owen L. Coon, 19 South LaSalle. The suit sought $30,000 in damages "for loss sustained by reason of the defendant's failure to transport cars of grain promptly and without delay and also for failure to transport the grain containers in the said cars without loss, all as agreed to be done by defendant." Like the other suits, this case was transferred to the United States District Court at the request of railroad attorneys, where it was settled out of court.

Soon, Owen found himself representing other grain dealers, including members of the Omaha-based Farmers National Grain Dealers Association. His caseload expanded dramatically in 1920 after a group of railroad yard workers walked off the job in April to protest working conditions. The unauthorized Switchmen's Strike of 1920 slowed freight delivery for six months, causing damage and delay to the farmers' shipments. Working out of the Transportation Building, at 608 South Dearborn Street, Owen took charge of the association's railroad claim department. He argued that the railroad was responsible for the spoilage of goods even during the labor strike and for the price drop caused by delays. He based this on a direct reading of the contract signed by the railroads and farmers—which was worded, perhaps not intentionally, in favor of the farmers.

"Owen Coon did not win without having quite a fight on his hands," *Finance* magazine reported. "He had to match wits with the best legal talent that the big carriers afforded. The railroads contended that, in light of the Switchmen's Strike, they were not liable under their contract for spoilage of products. The case came down to the detailed wording of the bill of lading contract. Owen Coon made such a strong case for the shippers that the railroads agreed to compromise. The compromise settlement was known as 'the case of the misplaced comma.' As the suits were handled on a contingent fee basis, the young lawyer was richly rewarded for the effort. In fact, it was from the fees received in these cases that he accumulated the money to go into the finance business."

Owen distinguished himself. He prepared a pamphlet that explained his work, and took on up to 600 claims. He sent the promotional material to Northwestern Law School Dean John H. Wigmore in 1920 to keep in touch with his old school. Owen said he had put the pamphlet together at night over a little more than two weeks. "I find in rereading it that the grammar in many cases is exceptionally poor and I would hate to think that it was the best I could do," he wrote to Wigmore. And yet Owen told Wigmore that the pamphlet was an essential education tool in his work. "The associations for whom I work thought that because of the unusually heavy losses that have been occurring and are now occurring that some kind of coordinated information on this subject should be drawn up and placed at the disposal of their members before the fall shipping season had progressed very far."

This pamphlet is distributed "almost entirely to farmers and country grain shippers, and you are the only one to whom I have entrusted a copy who could see the many defects," Owen wrote. Such mistakes "would not have been permitted to exist had more time been allowed to me, or the work been intended for use by the legal profession." Wigmore was so impressed by his former student that he asked Owen if he would consider being placed on the school's list of Illinois law lecturers. "My dear Coon," he wrote, "I looked over with deepest interest your pamphlet on claims by shippers against railroads. It is astonishing to me that you, in your short period at the bar, have been able to accumulate such a mass of experience and your systematic presentation of it is admirable and unique. I have handed the book to Mr. Kocourek for review in the *Illinois Law Review*." Owen appreciated Wigmore's support, and wrote that he hoped to find time in the coming year to reorganize his thesis and complete his Master of Laws degree. He never did find that time. Business beckoned.

‡   ‡   ‡   ‡

WHEN OWEN RETURNED to Northwestern Law School in 1918, following his year leave of absence, his parents Rose and James Coon moved to Evanston. They viewed this move to the Chicago area as only temporary, a way to be near Owen and to prepare their other son, Byron, for college. They enrolled Byron at Evanston Township High School, and expected to return to downstate Rantoul after he graduated in 1921.

But something happened that forever altered their plans—they became grandparents. And that put an end to any talk of moving. Rose felt especially close to her new granddaughter, Eleanor Rose Coon, who was Owen and Alice's first and only child, born in Evanston on February 3,

1921. According to family lore, James came in one day and said, "Rose, we are going back to the farm." Rose replied, "I'm not going." At which point, said Eleanor, her grandfather "slammed the door and went out and bought the Benson Avenue Garage to have someplace to go to work or do something."

So, in 1922, James and Owen signed a contract with Northwestern University to lease the eighty-four-stall Swan-Taylor Garage. They never intended to run it, only lease out the space. But they were later forced to take control of the garage when it failed. In 1924, James Coon started the Evanston Cab Company, headquartered in the garage at 1827 Benson Avenue in Evanston. He hired Northwestern University students to drive the cabs and incorporated the business on August 27, 1924, as the Evanston University Cab Company. The following month, James resigned as president of the company and Owen took over. It was the first of a series of businesses that would generate a fortune for the entire family.

James guided Owen and served as his business partner, but did not prop him up financially. "What money I have today, I have made myself," Owen wrote Eleanor in 1944. "Any money I borrowed from my father, I paid back to him with quite substantial interest. He repeatedly told me that such was the only way he could teach me to save—teach me to overcome all my problems as they came along, myself alone, if necessary—no matter what they might be! I had a father that I could run to for advice and counsel—but I never had a father that I could run to and ask for money—after the day I graduated from college." James believed strongly in modeling an economic independence for his son. "My father taught me that I must save something out of every dollar that I made—even if it was only a penny," Owen wrote in the 1940s. "Nevertheless, it must be something that must be saved—and that I must plan my life in detail, so that such would be the result." That was a lesson Owen never forgot. In another letter to Eleanor, he wrote: "Realize that lives must be planned—if they are to be successful—so that there is always something, no matter how small it may be, that is left over that can be put in the bank—that can be saved."

‡    ‡    ‡    ‡

ALTHOUGH HE ENJOYED GROWING SUCCESS, Owen retired from work as a practicing attorney in May 1924. He devoted himself to running the Evanston Cab Company and other businesses he began with his father.

James Coon, although retired from full-time work, had invested his savings in several businesses based in the Chicago area. The two men started or bought into at least five businesses involving cars—a garage, taxicab company, rental car company, oil and gas facility, and auto loan business. Four of the businesses failed quickly. The fifth was a success.

James and Owen Coon relied on their family to establish the early businesses. They hired Owen's first cousins, Ray and Lyle Titus, and his brother, Byron, who was nine years younger than Owen. During his years as a lawyer, Owen often sent Ray Titus out on the road to help drum up business among grain owners. Ray was to remain a trusted business colleague throughout Owen's life. By 1924, Byron had dropped out of Northwestern University's School of Commerce due to poor grades. Family legend has it that Byron was expelled after participating in a hazing incident that left a Northwestern student dead, but records show that Byron was no part of it. After Byron took a job pumping gas, Rose insisted that he be welcomed into the family business. It took years for Byron to earn Owen's complete trust as a businessman, but he did. Byron Coon and Lyle Titus both later served as presidents of General Finance Corporation, and Ray served as a vice president.

To get the cab business established, James and Owen purchased twenty-four cabs owned by Yellow Cab Manufacturing Company for $9,000 and bought older Checker cabs. Minutes of the January 27, 1925, meeting at the Coons's garage provide details that show how the early fleet was put together. "The condition of the taxicabs operated by the company was discussed, particularly the condition of the ten Checker cabs. As pointed out by Byron, the Checker Cabs are in such condition as to make necessary the immediate sale or trade of the same. Byron said he could make a trade of the Checker cabs to the R. F. Hall Taxicab Exchange for rebuilt A-2 Yellow cabs at a cost of $350 for each cab payable to Hall." By 1926, the cab business was well established, and Owen decided to cut back on his involvement. For at least one investor, this was not good news.

"I understand that you are contemplating getting out of the taxicab business and going back to your former profession of attorney," A. B. Southworth wrote on February 10, 1926. Southworth made it clear that he had invested in the cab company because Owen was running it. Now he wanted out. "I wish you much success in whatever line you may continue in," he wrote Owen, "and I want you to understand that my asking you to repurchase this stock is not a lack of confidence in the University Cab Company, but rather from the standpoint that I made this investment in the cab company while you were the head of it."

Owen bought back the stock, and kept his hand in the business. A new firm, University Cab Company, was incorporated on February 11, 1926, as a general taxicab business in Evanston, Chicago and Wilmette based at the 1827 Benson Avenue garage. Ray Titus was president. Coon remained as a major investor and attorney. These brown-and-tan cabs worked at the Loyola, Morse, and Howard elevated railroad stations in Chicago and at the Main, Davis, and Central elevated railroad stations in Evanston. They also worked out of the stops at the Davis and Central stations of the Chicago & NorthWestern commuter railroad.

The list of the firm's inventory offers insight into what it took to keep such a fleet on the road. The company started with the twenty-nine Model A-2 Yellow Cabs purchased from Owen's Evanston University Cab Company. Other inventory included jacks, lug wrenches, tire chains, gas heaters, batteries, a charger, spare brake bands, a grease gun, brake relining machine, bench lathe, pulley and belt, hoist and chain, electric drill, anvil, vises, oxygen tank, and an acetylene torch. The garage also had two barrels of grease, one barrel of alcohol, 350 gallons of gasoline, a gas pump and underground gas tank. Just in case, the company kept on hand one spare motor, differential and transmission, as well as spare hoods and fenders. And for the staff: thirty-three suit coats, twenty-nine robes, thirteen pairs of puttees, eleven caps, nine overcoats, and eight plaid trousers.

The Coons also started a rental car company out of the garage and incorporated it in 1924 as the Evanston Driverless Car Company. The name was changed to University Rent A Car Company the following year. In 1927, James Coon formed the Evanston Economy Oil Company to service cars and sell petroleum products. Yet by 1928, some of the Coon companies were struggling. The outside firm that had leased the garage folded, and Owen was having trouble running the garage, which repaired, painted, simonized, and washed cars.

Letters from the period show a great deal of strain. Owen wrote, "The American Garage is losing money every day and under such circumstances the only thing for me to do is to sell it as soon as possible. I cannot sell it, however, with the title in its present condition. In order to cut down my loss, please hurry this sale under foreclosure to as rapid a conclusion as possible. It is getting to be a matter of some serious consequence to me." And, in a similar manner, he wrote of the oil company, "I want to get rid of this corporation without having to go through very much red tape or expense doing it. The important thing that causes me to want to dissolve this corporation is to make sure that there is no liability on the part of the Evanston Economy Oil Company." The Coons were not afraid to start businesses and were not afraid to fail. That was a key to their success. Their spirit of enthusiasm and risk-taking was in part a spirit of these entrepreneurial times.

This willingness to take risks became especially obvious soon after James Coon was introduced to Robert Wilson, the operator of a small Evanston-based car finance company called Aetna Acceptance Company in Evanston. As *Finance* magazine explained in 1945, "The Aetna Acceptance, Bob Wilson explained, needed working capital, so it was proposed that if the Coons would take up to $25,000 each, it would be willing to pay one percent interest on monthly balances with chattel mortgages as collateral." The Coons agreed to loan the money on a trial basis.

Owen became engrossed in the credit business. "The business arrangement worked fairly well but it required the handling of a lot of collateral, with records being kept of the schedule of payments, past due paper and defaults," *Finance* wrote. "Owen Coon personally checked the collateral in his office on LaSalle Street and thus gained a firsthand knowledge of finance company operations. In setting up the records and keeping track of the payments, the young lawyer observed that repossessions were few and the ratio of losses impressively low for a credit carrying a twelve percent interest return. He decided this was a much better business than practicing law."

Owen's daughter, Eleanor, tells a similar story. After Wilson quickly repaid the $25,000 loan, "My grandfather said, 'Let's go down and see how he did it.' The man was loaning money on cars. My grandfather said, 'If he can do it, we can do it.'"

James and Owen formed a partnership, the Evanston Motor Acceptance Company, with one desk. On March 1, 1925, they each invested $50,000 in cash to form an automobile finance company. The firm was incorporated two years later. In 1928, the firm changed its name to the Motor Acceptance Company. Wrote Owen: "My father spent all of his active business life at Rantoul, and gradually accumulated a sizable

29

competence. One-half of the original capital of the Motor Acceptance Company, out of which the present General Finance Corporation grew, was the result of his work and effort in Rantoul, Illinois." For the Coons, this was the formula: Small town experience and savvy combined with big city risk-taking creates a Chicago dream.

‡　　‡　　‡　　‡

THE FIRST GASOLINE-POWERED AUTOMOBILES, known as motorcars, were produced in the final years of the nineteenth century. In 1901, Ransom E. Olds started making what he called Oldsmobiles, and cars began being built in quantity. These first automobiles were sold to well-to-do customers, who paid cash for their remarkable new toys. Demand in those early days exceeded supply. Dealers generally sold cars as soon as they received them. Since most car buyers were wealthy, financing of cars was hardly considered. But in 1908, Henry Ford proclaimed that he had mass-produced a "car for the multitude." At half the cost of the coupes and broughams of the day, the Model T, at $850 to $1,000, was within the financial reach of many Americans. Few had the cash to make outright purchases, so car industry leaders figured out a credit system, known as installment or time-sales. Eventually, more than 18 million Tin Lizzies were sold.

The car industry moved sluggishly in its first decades because both potential dealers and potential customers simply didn't have enough money. But when sales finance companies came into existence, the industry quickly picked up speed. The history of America's love affair with cars, writes author Lendol Calder, often neglects to mention the key aphrodisiac—consumer credit. "Without credit financing, the automobile would not so quickly have reached, and perhaps never have reached, a true mass market, and its impact on American life would have taken a very different course," Calder writes in his 1999 book *Financing the American Dream: A Cultural History of Consumer Credit.* "Installment credit and the automobile were both cause and consequence of each other's success."

It took a while for the idea of purchasing cars on credit to take hold. The first auto finance company opened in San Francisco in 1913. Four years later, only twelve car finance companies existed in the nation. But then, almost overnight at the end of World War I, the car loan boom hit. By the 1920s, almost two-thirds of new cars and more than half of used cars were bought on credit. By the mid-twenties, car loans had changed our way of life. "We are living in an age of credit, or perhaps a more accurate delineation would be an age of debt," wrote George Horace Lorimer in a 1924 *Saturday Evening Post.* In 1925, when the Evanston Motor Acceptance Company was started, the number of finance companies peaked at nearly 1,500.

Bankers stayed out of the early auto financing industry because cars were problematic collateral. Automobiles could be moved and were difficult to track down. And the value of a car was difficult to determine because it was often based on the cost of reconditioning. Bankers, leery of giving credit to automobile dealers from the start, also shunned the paperwork needed for time-sales loans to consumers. "The depreciation between the price of a new car and the price of a secondhand car introduces a larger element of risk in connection with this time-payment method of sales and makes the financing more burdensome," Harry Tipper wrote in the May 25, 1922, issue of *Automotive Industries.* "Furthermore, this depreciation is complicated by the condition in which the owner keeps his car and the attention he pays to its servicing and maintenance."

*Automobile Industries,* the leading trade publication of the day, editorialized that more finance companies were needed to help car dealers secure loans. Auto manufacturers at the time generally required dealers to pay up to 40 to 50 percent in cash. "Financing the sale of motor vehicles, at wholesale and retail, is one of the big problems of the industry," the magazine wrote. "So long as manufacturers insist upon selling their products on a C.O.D. basis, their dealers will require longer lines of credit than businessmen of the same ability who sell other merchandise of equal value but who are given thirty or sixty days in which to meet their bills, thus having an opportunity to turn over a good share of the goods they sell before they have to pay for them."

These new car loan businesses both helped and hindered the early car industry. "Finance companies are not philanthropic institutions and they have their faults, but they are the best means developed thus far for financing time-sales when the dealer's bank won't handle the paper," *Automobile Industries* reported. But these early companies made transactions almost unpalatable because the deals were cloaked in complexity. "To most dealers, and to many manufacturers, the operations and the internal workings of a finance company are a profound mystery," the magazine reported. "Dealers kick on what they consider the extortionist rates charged for the service given. Unfortunately, the finance companies have done little to enlighten their patrons. Such attempts at enlightenment as they have made have been couched in language absolutely unintelligible to the average dealer. He will try to look wise and nod his head at the right time but it is all so much Greek to him. When the attempt at explanation is finished, the chances are that he will be more convinced than ever that someone is trying to put something over on him."

This was the scene that Owen Coon entered in 1925 when he started Motor Acceptance Company. Car dealers were having trouble consummating purchases because car buyers had trouble finding credit. The process delayed sales and limited the market. "Some uncertainty must exist at all times, but the operations of finance corporations, properly conducted, permit the removal of most of this uncertainty in the transaction of the business," wrote Harry Tipper. "The finance corporation, adequately capitalized and properly managed, dealing with thousands of individual purchasers, and with dealers in many sections, is in a position to develop actuarial statistics in connection with its work which will provide a proper balance between the charges of average losses so that the entire credit will be on a sound basis."

By the end of the twenties, phrases such as "Quick Money," "Easy Credit" and "Buy Now, Pay Later!" were an accepted part of American life, Lendol Calder noted. Consumer debt almost doubled during the decade. "The installment plan was to consumer credit what the moving assembly line was to the automobile industry," he wrote. "Without it, today's trillion dollar consumer credit industry would be inconceivable."

America had changed forever. Harvard economist Franklin W. Ryan wrote in 1930: "The American family's plunge into debt for commodities during the last few years constitutes one of the most remarkable phenomena in modern history." The installment loan, introduced during the 1850s by the Singer Sewing Machine Company to sell its treadle machines for a "dollar down, dollar a week," was perfected during the 1920s on cars. Under early auto installment plans, buyers put one-third of the car cost down and paid monthly installments for twelve months. This arrangement made for big profits for sales finance companies. They were permitted to skirt usury laws, which limited annual interest charges of six percent. That's because the sales finance companies did not make loans to buyers. Instead, the companies actually purchased installment contracts from car dealers.

"In the early 1920s the time price was 15 to 22 percent greater than the cash price: finance charges were typically 10 to 15 percent simple interest on the amount financed, dealer reserves ranged between 1 and 3 percent, loss reserves were about 1 percent, and insurance premiums were about 3 percent," wrote Martha L. Olney, author of *Credit as a Production-Smoothing Device: The Case of Automobiles, 1913-1938.* "Since the total amount due was usually spread over ten or twelve months, effective annual interest rate on the amount financed exceeded 30 percent."

The twelve-month payback period was not arbitrary, Calder wrote. "Repair bills after the first year often ran so high that finance companies were afraid car buyers would be disinclined or unable to pay their remaining notes. Security for the loans was given in the form of a chattel mortgage or a conditional sales contract. After the paperwork was completed, the dealer would call his finance company over the phone, a credit check would be conducted in a matter of hours, and the deal would be sealed or denied."

The Coons's Motor Acceptance Company fits well within this historical period, a time when the American Dreamer sat behind the wheel of a car. Auto finance companies such as Motor Acceptance helped America's young car industry flourish. Financial credit made automobiles a staple of American life. The Coons took advantage of Americans' desire to own a car.

The Motor Acceptance Company financed automobile dealers and purchasers. The company received money from banks, which were leery of making direct "tin-can loans." In this way, the banks did not risk money on individual loans. Instead, bankers loaned money to sales finance companies as they would make loans to any commercial institution.

But by 1926, one year after Motor Acceptance was created, the auto finance industry was in disarray. In addition to legitimate companies, the field was crowded with fly-by-night companies that had so tainted the auto industry that O. H. Cheney, vice president of the American Exchange-Pacific National Bank in New York, called installment sales "jazz economics." He wrote: "Good profits made by the earlier finance companies attracted a great many small, hastily organized concerns into the field and competition for the past two years may justly be described as cutthroat." Most companies liberalized borrowing terms in order to attract business. Few loan requests were rejected. But, Cheney said, the prosperous times have meant that money losses have been kept to less than one percent. "As a result of this competition, the automobile business today is no longer selling automobiles—it is selling installment contracts," he continued. "It is selling pieces of paper with a lot of legal verbiage which the buyer may or may not understand and which he may or may not be able to follow."

Easy money was creating a new society.

"There is no use running counter to a great current which has its source in the very wellsprings of human nature," wrote George W. Norris, governor of the Federal Reserve Bank of Philadelphia, in 1926. "In this country we have been enjoying for the last four years a period of great prosperity, during which the purchasing power of the masses has been greater than ever before in our history. We have a natural inclination or predisposition to buy, encouraged and developed by an incredible mass of seductive advertising. Hitherto this inclination has been curbed by lack of the money with which to pay. Now this barrier has been broken down.

"Who is to apply the brake?" he asked. "Not the dealer who finds that it increases his sales. Not the manufacturer whose god is quantity production. Not the credit company, whose livelihood is dependent on it. Not the bank, which finds the business profitable and knows that a competitor would be glad to get it."

By mid-1926, the financial credit industry had settled down and loans were being made with more logic. *Automobile Industries* reported that the practice of low down payments and long-term deals had diminished because many of the companies that once thrived on them had failed or merged. On July 8, 1926, the trade magazine headlined a story: "Frenzied Retail Financing Subsides; Sounder Methods Prevail."

The Coons made money two ways: providing money to car dealers and car buyers. Loans to dealers, called "wholesale financing," usually covered 80 to 90 percent of the invoice price and were due three months after the delivery of new cars from the factory. "The service offered by the company covers all forms of financing from the making of loans to refinancing old accounts with other companies and postponing payments or arranging for reductions," one trade journal wrote about Motor Acceptance. During the first year, the Coons's new company brought in $250,000 of this business.

The Coons also made money by "retail financing," making loans to car buyers. One of the keys to the early success of Motor Acceptance was that the company kept repossessions low by requiring a one-third down payment on cars. Borrowers had to fully pay back loans for used cars in twelve months and loans for new cars in sixteen months. "These very rigid restrictions automatically regulate and control the kind and type of paper which the company can discount from its dealer connections and assures at all times a type of collateral in the trust of the very highest caliber," a Motor Acceptance Company financial report stated.

Owen also kept the repossession rate low by only making loans in the local area. During the 1920s, Motor Acceptance only offered loans to borrowers in Winnetka, Wilmette, Evanston, Highland Park, Lake Forest, Park Ridge, Niles Center, Des Plaines, and the North Side of Chicago, an area that Owen called "one of the best credit districts that exists anywhere in the middle west, if not the entire United States." He wrote: "When repossessions do occur, the amount involved is small and the demand for such types of cars on resale is constant and steady." Some borrowers did default. "For years, my father used to only drive cars that were repossessed," recalled Eleanor. "He'd stop by the lot on Howard and Clark streets and pick out a car for a couple of days. It just wasn't important to him in those years what car he drove."

Here, according to papers filed with Coon's lawyer, is how the business evolved on a corporate level.

> On May 23, 1927, a $10,000 company was organized, called the Evanston Motor Acceptance Company, Inc.; 1,000 shares of $10 par stock was issued, 50 percent of which was owned by Owen Coon and 50 percent by James Coon, although the stock, when issued, was issued 997 shares to James S. Coon, one share to Owen Coon, one share to Byron Coon, and one share to Rose O. Coon.

> The corporation took over the business of the partnership and issued, as consideration, the 1,000 shares of stock above mentioned and gave notes to the officers for the balance of the book value of the partnership at that time. Everything was handled on a dollar for dollar basis and when the corporation started business it thus had a very small capitaliza-

tion and a heavy officers' notes payable as a liability. This corporation had only one class of stock, and it was an Illinois corporation.

Business went along on that basis and the name was finally changed to Motor Acceptance Company. In February of 1928, the Union Trust Company, with whom we were attempting to establish a line of credit at that time, extended us the line of credit, which was our first Loop connection, but only on condition that we cancel the officers' notes entirely and take in exchange therefor additional stock, so as reduce the liabilities and increase the capital structure. When such was done, there was $200,000 worth of shares of $10 par value common stock, half of which was owned by Owen Coon and half by James S. Coon, although at that time the stock record books show James S. Coon as the owner of 9,998½ shares and Owen Coon the owner of a similar amount, with one qualifying share in the name of Rose Coon, Alice Coon, and Lyle Titus.

Owen oversaw the entire loan business, and served as the day-to-day attorney until late 1930. Running the finance company was financially more rewarding than law work or the family's other ventures, but the work was overwhelming. Owen relied on his corporate attorney, former Northwestern classmate Dean Traxler, for commercial direction. Owen's letters to Traxler show the nitty-gritty involved with running a new business and the complexity of financing. For instance, in August 1927, Owen wrote: "Would you write me as to what errors I am making in the confession of judgments on notes? My father says that there are several things that apparently I am overlooking. Please advise me in detail what you had in mind either over the phone or by letter so that I can protect myself."

During those early years, the limits of the law were being defined for the new car credit industry. In November, Owen wrote Traxler, "What is your opinion as to my right to levy on the cash value of a life insurance policy of a man against whom I have a deficiency judgment for loss arising out of repossession and sale of an automobile. Can I do it or not?"

As an early founder of a car credit company, Owen was treading legal and economic water alone. "What shall we do: use the chattel mortgage or conditional sales contract?" he asked Traxler in one letter. "To use the chattel mortgage it costs us $1,200 or better a year in recording fees. On the other hand, the conditional sales contract is good security for considerable sums of money. The conditional sales contract is far easier to use, but is it safe? Let me know what to do and be sure if I get into trouble you will know how to get me out."

Owen had an excellent relationship with his attorneys and seldom questioned their advice or fees. But he was above all a businessman and always watched the bottom line. In 1930, he wrote Traxler about a $75 bill. "I have never complained about the charges you have made before, Dean, but I really think that your charge in this particular case is excessive. We had two conferences on the phone regarding this matter and neither one consumed more than four or five minutes at the outside." Traxler responded two days later with a long explanation, which concluded: "If, bearing my above explanation in mind, you still have a feeling that the figure is too high you can substitute any figure you desire for the figure named in our bill and we will accept your check and forget about it." Owen reduced the fee by $25.

Running a finance company was a formidable challenge. Owen had to keep his interest rates above the interest rates charged to him by banks. Moreover, he had to keep cars, the collateral, from slipping away. In 1926, for example, Owen's attorneys were instructed to track down the owner of a 1922 Marmon touring car in New York City. The firm sent a Western Union telegram to a New York law firm saying that a customer, named R. C. Parker, left Illinois without making the next payment with $545 due. The telegram stated: "Chief of police in Evanston has warrant for Parker's arrest for removing mortgaged property from Illinois and has notified chief of police in New York City to pick up Parker but no report received. Stop. Have Parker arrested and await instructions unless he pays up balance of $545 in cash immediately." The agent hired in New York quickly found the car, but he decided to use it for himself for a couple of days. He drove it until the car's differential broke. Motor Acceptance dispatched Lyle Titus to New York to fix and sell the car. The company spent $835, and sold the car for $450. This, of course, frustrated Owen, who became determined to track down Parker and have him pay for the loss. Two years later, Owen was still on the case. Motor

Acceptance located Parker working for Swift and Company in Cleveland, and Owen instructed his attorney to sue him in order to garnish his wages. It's not clear whether the money was ever repaid.

‡   ‡   ‡   ‡

BY 1927, Owen was running four companies: the Motor Acceptance Company; the University Cab Company; the American Garage, and the University Rent-A-Car Company, a company licensed under the Hertz Driveurself System. That year, Owen was charged with a curious crime—running a confidence game. He was arrested on September 14, 1927. In Case 171688: The People of the State of Illinois v. Owen L. Coon, he was charged with trying to sell a worthless diamond for $180 to a man named Pietro Rocca. It is not clear how serious the charges were, and scant records exist in Owen's legal files at the Chicago law offices of McDermott, Will & Emery. The case, before Judge William R. Fetzer, was dismissed for want of prosecution on September 29, but Owen had to pay costs. He also paid $1,000 bail money.

To this day, it remains unclear whether this case was a matter of mistaken arrest or a true low point in Owen's life. Nothing in Owen's past life, or future life, would hint at such activity, and it's difficult for anybody who knew Owen to place this incident into any sort of context. "It's hard to understand—it's out of character," said Eleanor decades later. She had never heard of the charges and found it incomprehensible. "I can't believe he was involved in something so chintzy," she said. "There was nothing cheap about my father." But it is clear that these were difficult financial times.

In 1928, Owen wrote attorney Traxler that he could just barely pay his attorney bills. The letter came after Owen traded a farm in Central Illinois that was owned by the family for a garage and service station in downstate Champaign. "I really am short of money in every quarter," he wrote. "Our Champaign deal took $15,000 and I had to pay off one particular line of $10,000 at a bank recently and we have had so many loans tendered to us in the finance business from automobile dealers that we had to buy whether we wanted to or not, so our bank balances look worse than sick and I am trying to get them built up to the minimum required by our banks in the next three or four weeks."

From the notes between Owen and Traxler, it is obvious that Owen understood early on how to take advantage of corporate rules. He wrote the attorney in 1928 that he wanted his wife, Alice, to become vice president of Motor Acceptance retroactive to July 1927. His lawyers went back into the minutes of July 23, 1927, and had Rose Coon resign so that Alice could be vice president. But that turned out to not be what Owen wanted. "What we desire is to have two vice-presidents; one, Rose O. Coon and the other Alice E. Coon, so that we can pay them both salaries. We do not want the resignation of Rose O. Coon as originally drawn up." These notes also reflected family disagreements. In the same note to Traxler, Owen wrote: "I also want to eliminate Byron S. Coon as a director of the company and instead of him have Lyle A. Titus as a director of the company as of today. I also desire Lyle A. Titus made treasurer of the company instead of James S. Coon."

Finance companies that managed to make it through these cut-throat days of the mid-1920s generally thrived. New car production peaked in the pre-Depression years. In 1929, a record 5.2 million cars were produced. These were boom times for most companies associated with the auto industry, including auto finance firms.

When the stock market crashed, leading financiers believed they might be immune to the worst of the national economic depression. In fact, the 400 members of the National Association of Finance Companies who met in Chicago in November 1929, four weeks after Black Thursday, predicted that their industry would help the nation recover. Economic analyst Milan V. Ayres declared that time-payment plans would come to America's rescue because people hit by the stock crash could buy on installment plans and pay over twelve months instead of paying cash up front. Remarkably, auto financing, which dropped nationwide in 1930, picked up again in 1931.

Owen Coon's little firm thrived during the late twenties and early thirties. By 1929, the Motor Acceptance Company had its head-quarters in the State Bank Building in Evanston. Its stationery boasted that the company had $250,000 in capital. That year, Owen fixed the salaries of the firm executives. James S. Coon was to receive an annual salary of $11,000 as president; Owen, serving as attorney and secretary, was to receive $20,000; Byron, as vice president, was to receive $11,875; Lyle Titus, as treasurer, $14,075, and Ray Titus, as a valued employee, $13,600. By 1931, Motor Acceptance Company stationery listed Owen as president, Byron and Ray Titus as vice presidents, Lyle as secretary. The stationery, from the State Bank Building, also listed an Oak Park office in the Forsythe Building.

‡    ‡    ‡    ‡

As THE FIRM PROSPERED in the matrimony of credit and cars, Owen's own marriage to Alice began to unravel. Documents left from years of unhappiness form a sad chapter in the lives of Owen and Alice Coon. Their divorce decree—Case No. 502219, Owen L. Coon v. Alice Wright Coon—was entered in Cook County Superior Court and signed by Judge Walter P. Steffen on August 19, 1929. Owen agreed to pay Alice $50 per week as alimony, and agreed to keep the amount open if Alice showed more need.

Many of the conflicts between Owen and Alice began as arguments over spending and credit, an obvious irony considering Owen's business ventures. Owen divorced Alice after she was diagnosed as schizophrenic. She had become a drain on his professional life, and he felt that he could not help her. "My mother was beautiful, loving and kind, but she would give everything away while my father was trying to build something," said Eleanor, who was just a young child during the late 1920s. "My mother saw my father making money, and she started spending it," Eleanor said. "She would buy a bicycle for me, and she would tear up the bill. My father was trying to build credit in Evanston and my mother was tearing up bills." Decades later, Eleanor was sympathetic to both her mother and father as she looked back at their marriage. "He didn't know what to do with Mother," Eleanor said. "He was trying to stay alive."

Although the divorce proceedings did not mention Alice's condition, later court papers indicate that Alice started to show mental derangement in the spring of 1928. On October 1, Owen took Alice to North Shore Health Resort in Winnetka, where she was confined for treatment of mental illness. Three days later, Owen filed a petition alleging that Alice was insane and that she needed to be committed to a hospital or asylum. On October 6, Owen took Alice to the Milwaukee Sanitarium at Wauwatosa, Wisconsin, where she remained confined until December 22. Eleanor said that her mother was tied to a bed and that her hair turned white. Alice was brought back to the North Shore Health Resort, where she stayed twelve days. She was removed and placed in private care, first in an Evanston apartment and then at an Evanston hotel. She was then taken to an apartment, where she lived with a special nurse until August 1929. "She remained mentally sick and deranged and incapable of conducting her own affairs," the court later determined.

It was Alice who actually started the divorce proceeding. Alice's sister, Abigail Wright, was living at the Coon house in 1928 and witnessed the deterioration of their marriage. She was interviewed by Dean Traxler, Owen's attorney, who made the following notes:

> Thursday July 12, 1928, at 418 Church St. Evanston morning—7:30 a.m.
> Altercation over buying a rug. Owen didn't want her to buy it—before breakfast—in bed room while dressing. Sister Abbie Wright was living with them, and was in bath room—adjoining bed room, direct view—altercation continued from day before—Owen slapped Alice, who ran out of room, ran into kitchen and locked door.
>
> Monday—July 16, 1928
> Alice wanted a dress at MF & Co. [Marshall Field & Company]—so she was going to write a check for it, and Owen told her not to do it—After dinner, 7:30 p.m.—418 Church Street, Evanston in living room. Picked up an ash tray and threw it at her. Hit her on the shoulder. Left black and blue mark. Sister Abbie Wright in den (opens off living room), saw it all, ran to Alice and called Owen a big brute. Owen leaves the house and never returned.
>
> Saturday—July 21, 1928
> At Manteno, Ill. at Alice's parents—Owen went down to patch it up. Evening 8:00 p.m. Kitchen, after dinner. Sister Abbie Wright there—Owen at first suggesting spending night at house he was renting in Manteno. Alice said it wasn't fixed up—made Owen mad, said he was thru with her and pushed

her against doorjamb—hit her back. ...lamed her up
and she was in bed for two days.

In 1928, Alice began divorce proceedings by preparing formal charges against Owen. As a woman filing an equity case, she was known in those days as an "oratrix." Her case read:

—July 12, 1928: Defendant struck your Oratrix violent blows with his fists.

—July 16: Defendant threw an ashtray at your Oratrix, striking her in the shoulder and causing black and blue marks to appear upon her person.

—July 21, 1928: Defendant pushed your Oratrix violently against the edge of a door, injuring her back and causing her to be confined to her bed for a period of two or three days.

The suit was never filed.

Handwritten letters from Alice to Traxler show that Alice was a deeply troubled woman. Alice wrote the attorney that detectives were constantly watching her and that she had a connection to royalty. For decades after these early problems, Alice hallucinated about being part of a major crime. There is little doubt that Alice suffered severe psychological problems during the last several years of her marriage. "She was a schizophrenic," Eleanor said. "I believe she suffered from severe postpartum depression. You can see it on her face in pictures of her after I was born. It's a whole other look."

Owen did not understand his wife's struggles, Eleanor said, and did not show enough patience. "He just wanted to get on with life." And, she said, Owen was terrified that Alice might ruin his credit rating, which he felt had to be perfect because he was in the finance business. "I think he was also afraid of mental illness because he told me he slept with his leg across my mother before he left her," Eleanor said. "My mother wouldn't hurt a flea; she wouldn't hurt anything. I think he was afraid that she might. They had such a different feeling about mental illness than they do now."

Owen had cause to worry. Alice's sister, Charlotte E. Wright, twenty-two, committed suicide in 1927 by inhaling gas in an Evanston apartment. She had been a nurse at the Evanston Hospital. Owen wrote frequently that he worried about the mental stability of the Wright family.

On July 6, 1929, Owen filed a bill for divorce against Alice, charging her with abandonment. Six weeks later, the divorce was granted. The break-up added to Alice's problems. In the late summer of 1929, she was sent to Wichita, Kansas, where first she was confined to Wichita Hospital and then taken in by her sister, Helen L. Seltman. Eleanor believes that Helen told Owen that she would take care of Alice if he paid her $150 per month. "He sent money and she pocketed it and doled it out to a lady who tied her to the bed for two years," said Eleanor, who learned of this when she visited her mother in Wichita on a weekend the daughter will never forget. "My Aunt Helen made money off of my mother," she said, "as God is my witness."

When Eleanor and Alice's mother, Elizabeth Wright, went to visit Alice in Wichita, Alice pleaded with them to be released. "My mother took me in a room and said, 'Get on your knees in front of your father, and tell him to come and get me,'" Eleanor recalled. "I was ten. I went home and told my father. He sent my Grandmother Coon to get her, and they brought her to the North Shore Hotel. My father did not know what to do." Eventually, Owen found a caretaker for Alice near her Manteno, Illinois, relatives. She lived in the home of Belle Wright, a cousin, and then moved into a private house.

Although Owen showed kindness toward Alice, he was severely criticized for the way in which he handled the divorce. He had told the judge that Alice had abandoned him, which was not true. Years later, Alice, through a guardian, sued Owen to declare the divorce void. In the 1929 divorce proceedings, Owen testified that Alice had not lived with him since December 1926, and that she refused several of his requests to live with her. He called his father, James, to the stand to corroborate the story. Later testimony showed that Owen and his father had lied. "Alice did not desert Owen as alleged in the bill, but the parties lived as husband and wife all of the time, from December 11, 1926, to August 19, 1929," the court later ruled. Owen had the duty to apprise the court that Alice was insane, the court stated. Instead, he fraudulently concealed this fact and got her to sign papers that ended the marriage while she was under his "absolute control."

Then, Owen dragged his feet in paying alimony—peculiar behavior for a man who prided himself in paying off every loan he ever received on time. During the first years after the divorce, Owen tried to get his monthly alimony check reduced, arguing that he was paying more than "reasonable maintenance." His plans were thwarted by a lawsuit, instigated by Belle Wright in 1935. To settle, Owen agreed to pay Alice a lump sum of $650 and give her future monthly alimony checks of $150 instead of $50 per week. Judge Joseph Sabath agreed to Owen's proposal, but—for some reason—Owen was late on paying the first checks in 1936. It wasn't until Alice's Kankakee lawyer, H. H. Wheeler, wrote to Owen's attorney threatening to report the missed payments to credit agencies that Owen took the court order seriously. "I certainly do not wish to take any action in this matter, but will be forced to do so unless he pays up," Wheeler wrote. That solved the problem. At least temporarily.

# CHAPTER THREE

# Sponsoring Dreams

---

"I WANT US TO PRODUCE MEN WHO CAN SELL THEIR
IDEAS IN COMMITTEE MEETINGS—TO BOARD OF DIREC-
TORS, AMONG EMPLOYEES AND AMONG ASSOCIATES IN
ALL WALKS OF LIFE—AND THUS BE ABLE TO INFLU-
ENCE 'HUMAN ACTION' ALONG PROPER LINES."

Less than a year after his divorce from Alice Wright, Owen Coon married Louise Walker. Louise sold perfume at a Walgreens drug store in the State Bank Building, home of the Motor Acceptance Company. Owen ate lunch at the store and the two became close friends. They married on March 22, 1930, seven months after Owen's divorce was finalized. The match was unusual, especially in that day, in that Owen married beneath his financial class.

Owen had expressed interest in several North Shore socialites after his divorce, but Louise was far different. She had grown up in Silverwood, Indiana. She went to school only through the fourth grade, but was smarter than her formal education might suggest. As a young woman, she had moved to Chicago with her mother and older sister, Pauline Dowdell. She had married Harry Walker, a salesman who had flown with Captain Eddie Rickenbacker in the 94th Aero Squadron in World War I. Harry was shot and shell-shocked in the war and slowly deteriorated mentally after the war. He was committed to the Elgin State Hospital before 1930 because of mental instability. The couple had one son, Harry.

Owen and Louise had much in common, Eleanor noted. Both had children. Both had been married to people who had suffered severe mental illness. "All this grief must have drawn them together," Eleanor said. "I'm sure Owen married Louise because she had a boy a year younger than me who could roller skate on the streets of Evanston after school.

She knew the value of a dollar because she was working in a Walgreens. And I was horribly spoiled. Imagine: I said to her one time, 'Keep the change, you need it more than I do.' She could hardly wait to get her hands on me. He married her to have a home and to have someone to take care of his daughter, so he could work."

Louise raised the children with strict rules. "She used to tell me stories about how she had to stand on a box and wash dishes," Eleanor recalled. "You could never have anything to eat after school, and she put a lock on the refrigerator to make sure."

For some reason, Owen's mother, Rose Coon, disliked Louise from the first day they met. Eleanor is not sure why. Owen's father, James, however, thought Louise would be a perfect companion to help Owen rebuild his life. Perhaps Rose resented the fact that James lavished attention on Louise. But Louise made it possible for Owen to be a successful businessman. "He dearly loved her because of the life she made for him," said Eleanor. "Mom was a wonderful lady," said Owen Coon Jr., who was born on January 21, 1932. "She spurred my father on to everything he did. She did not have an advanced education, but she created a businessman's house."

Little Harry Walker, born June 23, 1922, still recalls the day in 1930 he met Owen Coon at his mother's apartment on North Kenmore Avenue in the city. "I was in my little fire engine," said Harry, who was seven or eight years old. "Owen walked in and I followed him because he went to our apartment. I was curious, wondering who's this big guy coming in here? He looked down at me and I said: 'You're ringing our bell.' I'll never forget saying that. He made friends with me at that point and from that point he was the best friend I ever had in my entire life." On December 18, 1934, Owen filed a petition to adopt Harry Harold Walker after the death of the elder Harry Walker, who had succumbed to pulmonary tuberculosis at Elgin State Hospital at age forty-seven in 1933. Little Harry took the name Harry Harold Coon.

Owen and Louise lived in Evanston during the first years of their marriage, and then bought a home at 150 Park Avenue in Glencoe in 1933. Louise did the house over and added sparkle with her fine silver and Dr. Wall porcelain collection. But the change was difficult for Louise. "My father should not have moved her to Glencoe because she couldn't drive," Eleanor said. "She had only one friend up here and the people rejected her because she had come from Walgreens. They were all snobs."

Blending the two families was not easy. Louise had particular problems raising Eleanor, who Harry Coon recalls was something of a daredevil. "We'd go to Riverview Park and she'd be the first one to sit in the first seat of the rollercoaster," he said. What made Eleanor more difficult was the fact that she was not used to parental discipline. After Alice left, Eleanor had nearly complete freedom, even though she was still a child. "I used to get ten cents by signing my name so that I could go to the movies," she said. "I was in charge of myself."

The other challenge that Louise faced was what she viewed as the overindulgence of grandmother Rose. In 1943, Owen wrote an angry letter to Rose in which he criticized the "extreme attachment" that had developed between his mother and his daughter. Their relationship, he wrote, prevented Louise and Owen from exercising discipline in a proper and effective manner.

"In the period that intervened between the time that I left Alice and began the reestablishment of a home with Louise, you took care of Eleanor, Mother, and your kindness and help in doing so was then and still is greatly appreciated," Owen wrote. "You helped me bridge the gap. In doing so, however, you became unusually attached to Eleanor, because it is only natural for people as they grow older to become attached to younger people. This attachment, while excellent in itself, became probably the real cause of my problem with Eleanor—which has developed into a problem of our relationship together as mother and son. Because, in due course, Eleanor began to use such attachment to solve her own disciplinary problems, which developed gradually as she grew older in my home—disciplinary problems no different than those of any other child."

Owen wrote that Eleanor was difficult to mold. She did not take suggestions easily, and infrequently followed through when given advice from elders. "In the raising of Eleanor I had only one primary goal and that was to make sure she did not grow up like her mother: with the characteristics of selfishness, lack of self-control, and misrepresented statements about many things—the three characteristic that I mentioned in my letter to you about Alice—the characteristics that I came to loathe and that I was determined should not prevail as dominant characteristics in the life of my daughter." Owen's fear that Eleanor would take on her mother's worst qualities shaped his views on discipline.

After marrying Louise, Owen asked his new wife to take a strong hand in raising Eleanor. "I had to be away much of the time and in due course I had to start spending at least half of my time—or more—in Detroit," Owen wrote. "Our business was growing and developing at the time. Perhaps if I could have spent more time at home this problem might not have developed. In any event it fell upon Louise to do much of the work of raising Eleanor and to attempt to correct the characteristics mentioned above whenever they showed up in Eleanor even as a child because, after all, the characteristics of a mother are bound to be carried through to a certain extent into the life of a daughter." Owen wanted Eleanor to grow up in the mold of Louise, but grandmother Rose made that difficult. Owen and Rose disagreed on how much discipline was necessary in raising Eleanor. He wrote his mother:

> Perhaps I desired too strongly to reach this goal. If so, I am willing to accept the criticism. Whenever I saw any of these characteristics show up in Eleanor's actions, both Louise and I took prompt steps, by discipline, to attempt to force the exclusion of such characteristics from her personality. But it seemed that any discipline we put on Eleanor only resulted in her running to you for relief—with you calling me and complaining about how I was treating "poor Eleanor."

> At first, I would complain to Louise and suggest that she should do things differently, but finally I realized that Louise was doing just what I asked her to do and was getting herself in the middle between you and Eleanor solely at my suggestion and through my asking her to follow the above mentioned policy in the raising of Eleanor. Then finally, as time went on, in order to please you and not cause too much of a ripple in our family relationship, Louise and I started to give in. We gave in on this—and on that—and therein lay my mistake. I should not have given in! I should have demanded then that you stay in your own back yard and let me raise my daughter as I alone thought it best to do.

The result, Owen wrote, was that he and Louise were pulling Eleanor in one direction, while Rose pulled her in another.

Owen clearly blamed Rose for undoing the discipline that Owen and Louise attempted. He wrote Rose that her relationship with Eleanor was "the strongest deterrent in our endeavor to teach her to think straight, talk straight, and be honest." Examples were plentiful, Owen wrote. When Louise set a limit on how many dresses Eleanor could wash each week, Rose stepped in and sent out Eleanor's excess laundry. When Owen set a limit on the number of shoes Eleanor could own, Rose called to complain he was not treating her fairly. "This action on your part—and the illustration I am using—is only one of many that I might give to you, and immediately fostered in Eleanor the knowledge that she could get around discipline in her home by simply going to you with her troubles. This set of circumstances started Eleanor on a path that led to lack of self-control, secretiveness, and misrepresentation to Louise and myself of what was going on as she attempted to cover up what was done by you and by her as you attempted to get around the home discipline that Louise and I were attempting to impose." In sum he argued, "Because of this lack of cooperation between all of us there is little wonder that in some cases the child did not know which way to turn. I blame myself for this confusion. When I saw it I should have eliminated contact of Eleanor with yourself."

Owen wrote that Louise had said, "Owen, you correct Eleanor. Leave me out of it. It makes your mother and Eleanor both hate me." But Owen told Louise to keep working with him. "So we kept at it and at it," Owen wrote Rose. "Eleanor developed the habit of telling you her troubles. Now and then she would stay with you over weekends and it would take until Wednesday of the following week to get her straightened out. Your sympathy for Alice, your reaction against Louise and myself (instead of working with us) all made Eleanor increasingly difficult to bring up with characteristics like Louise as compared to Alice."

Meanwhile, Owen felt that Alice's relatives, who took care of Eleanor for several months each summer in downstate Manteno, also were working against his efforts to impose discipline. "It was not until a year ago that we discovered that the Wright family (notwithstanding all the things I had done for them—with Mrs. Wright still living on the money I saved for the family) kept filling Eleanor's mind as she grew up with derogatory remarks about Louise and myself—telling her such things that Louise enticed me over the state line and made me marry her under threat of prosecution of me under the Federal Mann Act (can you imagine!!)—that Louise was a girl of loose morals, etc., etc. And yet, to fulfill my promise to George Wright, Louise and I faithfully kept Eleanor in touch with the Wright family." George Wright was Alice's father.

Given all of this, Owen's children had difficult childhoods. "I always loved him," Eleanor said. "He just never had time for all of us because he was trying to make us all safe." Owen Jr., proud to have his father's name, knows that the work and responsibility of running a company kept his father away. "He was living the life of an executive," Owen Jr. said. He does not resent the little time his father had for the family. "I didn't see much of my father because he was always traveling," Owen Jr. said. He recalls joyous—but few—moments with his father. He remembers his father tutoring him on mornings when Owen Jr. was in grade school and recalls going to the Homestead restaurant on Sundays before services at the First United Methodist Church of Evanston. Both went to Sunday school, Owen to teach and Owen Jr. as a student. But Owen Jr. also recounts moments when his father's work took precedence over fatherhood. "I remember playing football in the backyard while my father was on the phone," Owen Jr. said. "He was a very busy man. What time I did spend with him, he and I really enjoyed each other."

Rose Coon, for her part, was openly critical of how little time Owen spent with his children. "Owen used to give time to others' children, and now his need him greatly," she wrote to Owen and Louise during the 1930s. "Enter into their activities. It will give you more returns than any other investment. Try just one week and see if we can get a different slant on life in them. I would do anything I could for the children and am interested in their welfare."

Harry and Eleanor attended the Cranbrook and Kingswood Academies of Art near Detroit during the late 1930s. Harry was at Cranbrook for three years and Eleanor was at Kingswood, the girl's school, for two. They both flourished. Harry became a talented drummer, who, in Eleanor's words, was "as good as Gene Krupa." Eleanor became a successful student. Their father visited when he was in Detroit on business, which was often.

Eleanor returned to Glencoe in 1939 after graduating from the academy. She enrolled next at Ferry Hall, a finishing school associated with Lake Forest Academy. Owen wanted her to prepare there for Northwestern University, but after being away from home for two years Eleanor found it difficult to live with her parents again. In the fall of that year, she fell in love with Louis Scott, a student at the University of Illinois in Champaign. She ran away and got married on December 30, 1939.

It was truly a time of major changes for the family. In that same year, James Coon, the family patriarch, died. He had suffered from hardening of the arteries and needed outside care for much of the 1930s as his health deteriorated.

‡     ‡     ‡     ‡

THE MOTOR ACCEPTANCE COMPANY prospered during the Depression. By 1930, the company had more than $1 million in assets and was headquartered in a suite of offices on an upper floor of the State Bank Building. "On September 21, 1931—the day England went off the gold standard—our company adopted a voluntary policy of reducing volume, and all active solicitation of business ceased at that time," Owen wrote in the 1932 Motor Acceptance Company audit report. "It was our conviction that conditions were too unsettled to be solicitous about investing even an average amount of money. We believed that it was more conservative to forget volume and profits and be concerned primarily with maintaining at all times a good balance sheet with capital and surplus intact."

Owen realized that the key to running a successful loan company was to remain in excellent standing with the commercial banks that loaned him money. And he did not want to risk that reputation in the difficult years of the Depression. "During the last nine months we could have purchased more paper with a much greater immediate profit—but the result of such a policy might have been to show an unsatisfactory balance sheet at certain times in the past or future," Owen wrote. "We have chosen the more conservative route—realizing that if our balance sheet were maintained in proper condition throughout the remainder of the present depression, there would be abundant opportunities in the future to more than make up the loss of present profits." But business continued to be good. "While not actually soliciting business, we have still continued to purchase all good paper that has been tendered to us. Enough volume in the last nine months has been voluntarily offered to us from our old contacts, without solicitation, to keep capital and surplus intact and make a slight profit."

At the end of 1933, Owen summarized the successful first years of the company. "Motor Acceptance Company has a particularly interesting operating record," he wrote. "Average earnings on net worth during the nine years of its existence have been 16.8 percent. This includes four years of depression. . . . There has been a constant increase in capital and surplus in each year of operation—such increases coming entirely out of earnings. Never once for any year has there been a decrease in net worth." The company's success meant huge money. In 1933, Owen was paid $14,050 in salary and $23,777 in bonuses. Byron was paid $3,500 in salary and $4,592 in bonuses. James Coon was paid no salary, but received $14,842 in bonuses.

Remarkably, the Depression years were good years for most of the finance companies that survived because cars became an essential part of American life. To attract more customers, finance companies lengthened repayment schedules to two or more years and decreased the amount of down payment. Auto loans increased from $356 million in 1932 to $1.4 billion four years later. "Surprisingly, very few installment debtors found it impossible to meet their obligations," author Lendol Calder wrote of the 1930s. "Delinquent accounts became more common after 1929, and more people defaulted entirely, but the rates for delinquency and default remained very low, especially when compared with those of commercial loans."

Only 1 of every 200 borrowers was seriously late in paying monthly car loans in mid-1930, Calder found. "This was a considerable increase from a year earlier, but still remarkably low," he wrote. "And delinquency only rarely led to outright default and repossession." The reason, he wrote, was because of the severe consequences of defaulting on an auto loan. "Under the law, installment sellers owned a prior lien on installment goods," Calder wrote. "This meant that if the buyer defaulted on payments and the merchandise was repossessed, buyers lost the goods *and* the money they had paid in." That made quite an incentive to keep paying until the end.

In 1934, the Motor Acceptance Company moved into larger offices in the State Bank Building. Business increased dramatically that year, due primarily to the National Recovery Act, which spurred the sale of cars. "Purchase of cars has been nearly 100 percent greater this February than last," Owen wrote. "We have been compelled to move into much larger quarters to properly handle the business that is tendered us. With an increase in capital stock, we can still further expand the business."

Much of Owen's success was due to Paul L. Morrison and Arthur W. Newton. Morrison, a Northwestern University finance professor, would come to the house in Glencoe most every Saturday morning to give Owen ideas and tips. "My dad would pick his brain, and they greatly enjoyed each other's company," Eleanor said. Newton, a First National Bank of Chicago vice president, was one of the progenitors of the automobile finance industry. He envisioned the importance of consumer credit in making possible the mass production of cars, and he advised and lent money to Owen's company. "My father got crushes on people," Eleanor said. "They were not emotional relationships, but he depended on bright people." Owen paid Morrison $50 per session, and later wrote that he was much indebted to both men.

In late 1933, a small loan company in Detroit named General Finance approached Owen to help steer its financial future. The directors of General Finance asked him to serve as a consultant because the company was posting few profits despite possessing hundreds of thousands of dollars in capital. Because the company had become financially stagnate, General Finance needed help getting lines of credit from Detroit banks. "Hearing of the job Owen had done in Chicago with Motor Acceptance, the principal stockholders of the Detroit company invited him to tell them what was the matter with their company," *Finance* magazine wrote. "He pulled no punches and talked plainly and critically of how the company was being run. Evidently they were impressed because they listened with interest to his analysis and asked him to make a proposition under which he would be willing to take over the management." He did.

The company was transformed quickly under Owen's rule. "Owen Coon has plenty of spunk," *Finance* wrote. "One day, about four months after he started to run the company, he called a meeting of the principal stockholders and informed them that he proposed to fire all the other officers in the organization. While this bold proposal met with strong opposition at first, the group of stockholders agreed because, in view of the way that the company had been going, they had little to lose and everything to gain. The move stopped the 'playing of politics,' cleared out dead wood and the company started to make money."

*Time Sales Finance* magazine told a similar tale. "By 1934 Motor Acceptance had built its capital up to $500,000 and Owen Coon had won a reputation as a smart, resourceful operator," the magazine reported. When Owen was asked to assess the company, "he did with characteristic Coon candor." Owen accepted the board's request to take over the management of General Finance. He was formally hired on June 23, 1934, on an eighteen-month contract to run the company and serve as president. It was a remarkably high-stakes contract, reflecting Owen's confidence. He agreed to work for nothing—on a "no cure no pay" basis—but with the understanding that he was to receive 25 percent of the net profits, after the company paid all taxes and dividends on the preferred stock.

Owen immediately began to negotiate large loans. "He was able to fulfill these conditions because of the confidence of lending banks in his ability to operate the company profitably," wrote *Finance*. Within three months, Owen had arranged $650,000 in lines of credit at low interest rates from the three largest banks in Detroit. "As part of the deal," the magazine reported, "he gained an option at an attractive figure on 100,000 shares of common stock of the company. When he told Arthur Newton of the deal he had made, the sagacious Chicago banker insisted that he had driven too good a bargain and made him go back to Detroit and voluntarily give up a part of the stock option."

Owen put his profits back into the company by purchasing more stock and soon won permanent controlling interest in the company. General Finance surged, and in 1935 the Detroit company merged with Motor Acceptance, canceling Owen's employment contract. The assets of Motor Acceptance were transferred to General Finance and the new company took the General Finance name. Shares of General Finance Corporation and its sister company, General Discount Corporation, were distributed to Motor Acceptance Company stockholders after the merger was made official on December 2. Owen Coon and his family, including cousins Ray and Lyle Titus, ended up owning 72 percent of the stock.

With offices now in the Chicago and Detroit areas, General Finance faced a bright future, but was undercapitalized. "This meant that the company had two courses of action available to it," wrote Owen's attorney, Richard S. Oldberg. "One: to cut down the volume of business done and by so doing lose contacts with automobile dealers which would be extremely difficult to revive; the other: to obtain additional working capital. Realizing the seriousness of the situation, Owen Coon began negotiations in November 1935, before the merger was actually consummated, but when it appeared certain that it would be, to obtain additional working capital for the company."

Owen met with the investment firms Jackson & Curtis of Massachusetts, First Michigan Corporation and Charles A. Parcells Company in Michigan to obtain new loans. In 1936, the company issued $750,000 worth of subordinated debentures to raise more money. A subordinated debenture is an unsecured bond that companies with strong cash flows sometimes issue to raise cash. This was the first time that a finance company offered subordinated debentures to the public, which is now a common practice. And it was the first of many times that Owen figured out new ways to raise or lend money. "Owen Coon, upon several occasions, demonstrated that he has a most ingenious mind by finding practical, workable solutions for financial problems," *Finance* wrote.

Prior to the merger, Owen and his close associates were working for two companies. "Motor Acceptance Company was paying my salary, and yet I was spending half to two-thirds of my time on affairs other than those of Motor Acceptance Company—namely spending my time in Detroit on affairs of General Finance," Owen wrote years later. The same was true for Ray and Lyle Titus. "We all treated the work which we did on General Finance for the profit of that company and its options, as one of the activities of Motor Acceptance Company, and all of the participation of profits and stock option, therefore, went through Motor Acceptance Company as the stockholders of that company were the ones entitled to it."

When they merged, Owen offered General Finance stock to the public. The company was first admitted to trading on the Chicago Stock Exchange in December 1936. At the time, General Finance was a comparatively small corporation. It attracted little public notice during its first years on the market.

‡     ‡     ‡     ‡

FEELING SUCCESSFUL AND FORTUNATE, Owen Coon made his first recorded donation to Northwestern in 1928. It was $2.50. He gave $25 to the school in 1930, 1931 and 1932, gave $250 in 1933 and $188 in 1934. The next year, he started making donations to a scholarship fund he set up at the school. By the time of his death, Owen had contributed $91,000 to the university and made provisions for millions more.

In 1933, Owen was named vice president of the Northwestern University Association and was honored in 1934 as the most loyal of 33,000 alumni. In 1936, he was named to Northwestern University's Board of Trustees, where he served until 1948, first under President Walter Dill Scott and then under Franklyn Bliss Snyder. During Owen's first term on the board, he took a strong stand in support of philosopher Paul Arthur Schilpp, who complained that he was denied a full professorship because of his public pacifism, an unpopular posture during the late 1930s. Owen urged him to stay, writing that the university needed "live wires" like him. Schilpp remained at Northwestern, thanks in part to Coon's letter. He became a full professor in 1950, and stayed at the school until his retirement in 1965.

Owen's increased commitment to Northwestern can be traced in his wills. In an unsigned 1932 will, he did not mention the university. Two years later, Owen wrote attorney Dean Traxler: "I also want to leave in my will the sum of $5,000 to the Northwestern University Foundation, the income from which is to be used as a part of the so-called Phi Gamma Delta Scholarship." This was the start of Owen's scholarship program.

On November 26, 1934, President Scott's assistant, Thomas A. Gonser, sent Traxler the first draft of a proposed endowment for scholarships in forensics, the art and study of formal debate and argumentation. The following day, Traxler suggested to Owen that he endow the Clarion Dewitt Hardy Scholarships in Forensics. Owen responded four days later that he liked the idea. He wrote that he wanted to offer four full scholarships to freshmen or four half scholarships that would expand to full scholarships as the students progressed through Northwestern. The program was directed toward students who could not afford the $300 yearly tuition. Owen wrote that he hoped he could expand the program in the next four to five years to eight full scholarships if he was "reasonably successful."

Clarion Dewitt Hardy, Owen's debate coach, was born on a farm in Iowa, and attended rural grade school and high school in Denison, Iowa. He received a Bachelor of Arts degree in 1903 from Dakota Wesleyan University in Mitchell, South Dakota, and distinguished himself as the winner of state and interstate oratorical contests. He continued his training at the Cumnock School of Oratory, later the Northwestern School of Speech, and now the School of Communication, and received his master's degree in 1905.

Hardy returned to Dakota Wesleyan as a professor of oratory. He also served as chairman of the university's English literature and public speaking departments. Hardy came back to Evanston in 1911 to teach at the Evanston Academy, Northwestern's preparatory school, and serve as Northwestern's debate coach. He was promoted to Northwestern University in 1913 as a professor of English and public speaking. He resigned in 1920 to join the publicity department of Swift and Company, but returned to Northwestern once again five years later to resume his work as a professor in public speaking and debate.

Owen wanted Professor Hardy to run the forensics scholarship program as long as he was an active professor. "I want him to have a direct personal interest in the operation of the plan, and I want to have his influence felt in the training of the boys who receive such scholarships," Coon wrote of Hardy. "By this means, I hope to make more certain that he will pass on and do for those boys who are the recipients of such scholarships what he did for me in the years 1913, 1914, and 1915." Owen suggested his program be called the "Clarion DeWitt Hardy Scholarships in Forensics, the gift of Owen L. Coon in honor of that Northwestern professor who as counselor, teacher, and friend, contributed the most to his education." Owen wrote, "Possibly no one, except him and me, has ever fully known what influence his teaching and counsel had on my own personal development. I am fully cognizant of it, however. The purpose of these scholarships is to have that same thing done by Hardy for some other boys, with myself helping to make possible the continuation of that particular influence."

Owen wanted his support of the scholarships to be clear so that recipients would understand just how profoundly a good teacher and a good education could shape a student. "This is probably not the proper wording," he wrote, "but what I desire to have accomplished is that there be some wording in connection with such scholarships such that any Northwestern alumnus learning of them will understand the reason why I am giving such scholarships, and may thereby realize more fully their responsibility for passing back to Northwestern something of what they may have gained in future life from some professor or group of professors who made possible that training and accomplishment on their part. I want something in the way or wording which will make the recipient of such scholarship understand automatically the reason why he is getting such a scholarship and may also implant in his mind the idea in future years of doing likewise."

Owen believed that education was a foundation for professional and personal advancement. He wanted to promote forensics at the university because it was good training for future life. "Dr. Hardy developed in me a talent and a duty—the talent to express myself well in the pursuit of my aims, and the duty to use that talent to some degree in service to my fellow men," he wrote.

When Northwestern's Thomas Gonser informed Hardy of Owen's plan in December 1934, Hardy was startled because he had communicated with Owen only a few times since Owen's graduation. "The thought that my humble contribution could move a former student to do what you propose produces a satisfaction that reaches as near to completeness as one can get in professional life," Hardy wrote Owen. "But the personal element is a passing incident only. What you are going to do, if properly administered, is just the type of contribution that education most needs and gets too little of. A university must have a library, classrooms and laboratories—the more complete the better. But they will never make a great university in which to get an education. The heart of a university is at the point of the relationship between able students and great teachers. Get this last combination and you get the great institution."

Owen's December 29, 1934, reply to Professor Hardy is perhaps the most detailed written explanation of the scholarship program. "As long ago as 1921, I had decided to do something at some time, in recognition of what *I* knew *you* had done for *me*," Owen wrote. "Possibly, after all these years, I should explain certain reasons why I feel as I do toward you—and also why I am acting in this particular manner." Written on Motor Acceptance Company stationery from the State Bank Building in Evanston, Owen's letter recounted the experience he had as a Sunday school teacher at the First United Methodist Church and his hopes of influencing the future. Owen came to realize that he was not an especially good teacher of children. So he went on to teach church lessons at the Phi Gamma Delta fraternity house on the Northwestern campus. "You see," Owen wrote Hardy, "under my theology, I feel my life will have been wasted—unless somewhere, somehow, I obtain that certain 'follow through' upon the lives of others—perhaps a foolish idea for a supposed hardheaded business man, but nevertheless the thought has been there for several years now, seeking expression in some form."

Owen wrote that he had only one success—a student named Wally Cruice, who played right halfback for the varsity football team. "He would probably have been a success anywhere, any place, and under any conditions," Owen wrote. On the whole, Owen felt his work with college boys had been a failure. He improved the moral outlook of only a few of the young fraternity brothers, but did manage to get Phi Gamma Delta in good financial shape. In one month, he helped the fraternity brothers make $600 in investments. Instead of teaching them about God, he taught them how to make money—which was not his intention. "At any rate, it seems I just did not have time to be with the boys often enough —taking care of business too—to accomplish the proper results," he wrote. "Perhaps, I was impatient. Perhaps I wanted results too quick—and I guess I am not a teacher. After all, one probably cannot be a money maker and teacher too."

In June 1934, Owen started working fourteen to fifteen hours a day. He wrote Hardy: "[I decided] I would spend all my time on business to the exclusion of outside activities—work at it harder than ever—use my only apparent ability—namely 'making money' and try to connect up that ability with yours as a teacher to accomplish my goal—and what I know must be your goal as well." Owen's goal was to convey what Hardy had taught to others. Owen wrote Hardy that students must be taught:

### 1. How to "think straight."
Many is the time since I left school that I have re- called that expression of yours. I always think of it as I remember seeing you talk about it on a certain day in the classroom, while you stood on the north end of the platform in the large room on the second floor of the Old College. It is true, you said it many times, but such has always been the particular pic- ture that for some reason has lived with me. Many times when I did not know what to do I have said to myself "Stop—think this through—think it through straight, as Hardy would say." What it takes to keep teaching that idea, I do not know. That is, of course, your end of the job. Perhaps, it takes the training in debate that you used to give us. Perhaps, it is con- tinually harping on the idea. Perhaps, it is something else. I do not profess to know.

## 2. How to express and sell the ideas that are the results of "straight thinking."

I want us to produce men who can sell their ideas in committee meetings—to board of directors, among employees and among associates in all walks of life—and thus be able to influence "human action" along proper lines.

## 3. Their responsibility to others.

Their duty toward the university that gave them a developed mind. Their duty to bring more ethical principles into business. Their obligation to pass on to others something of what has been passed on to them. A proper concept of wealth and money and the realization that it is of value only as it is used to accomplish something either tangible or intangible that is of lasting benefit. A realization that the intangible is the hardest to obtain.

## 4. There is no substitute for hard work and long hours.

Many times have I remembered your frequent statement to me: "Coon, God did not give you a lot of brains or natural ability like Wickman. You must work hard. It may be a good substitute."

The much more difficult question still remains. What means are to be used to attain this goal—and satisfy the reasons for it? That is, of course, your part of the job. My job is to work hard, make money (and I just love to make it—not for the money itself—but just for the kick I get out of knowing that I can) and pass on part of it to you to carry out our joint project. I do not want to wait until we are both dead and buried before we can start on this project. I want to start it now—and see if we can lay the groundwork for it—so it will carry on better after we are gone.

Owen suggested a committee be formed to oversee the scholarship plan. That committee, he advised, would be composed of Hardy, the university president, the dean of the School of Speech, the director of personnel, and a professor appointed by Hardy whom Hardy would designate as his successor after he retired or died. Scholarship money was earmarked for students in financial need. Other worthwhile Northwestern students interested in forensics could participate in the program and would receive medals.

Owen realized that his scholarship program and legacy depended on the people who would execute and carry on the plan. "After all, money without personnel I have found in business is almost useless," Coon wrote. And he knew that he wanted his program to go beyond basic academics. "I want to know what is going to be done for that particular group of boys beyond the classroom," he wrote. "Are they to have loose morals? What will be done to mold their character, as well as their minds? I am not worried about their Latin, math, forensics, etc., such training is the easy part of the job. I am sure they will get that all right. They will be boys who will be above the average scholastically in high school to start with. They will keep up their scholarship to keep getting a scholarship year after year. Of all that I have no fear. But I do not want boys trained with my money, to be turned out with just 'trained minds.' The success of the project depends on how Hardy can figure out a way to improve the character of recipients."

Owen wrote Hardy several letters filled with plans and ideas. As a businessman, Owen was clear about outlining his objective for the scholarship program, and clear about his determination to reach that mark.

"If you fail, as I feel I have failed—then I must attempt some other method of obtaining the goal I seek," he wrote Hardy. "At Yale, or is it at Harvard, I hear that the students are being segregated into groups with a head teacher or principal living in a residence near the boys—to be more readily accessible and more of a companion to them. I wonder if it is not a move in the right direction—a move toward making more personal that relationship between teacher and student."

Northwestern had recently moved in the right direction when Dean James W. Armstrong put tutors in fraternity houses, Owen believed. But what are needed, he wrote, are the best men of the university with the leaders of the faculty in those houses. "Around the fireplaces of those fraternity houses and nowhere else I sometimes think is where the character of future Northwestern men will be built." Owen wrote that he sometimes pictured Hardy taking over the supervision of a fraternity house, a place like his Phi Gamma Delta. "At first, dropping in just to take meals with the boys at noon—gradually getting acquainted with the boys and soon becoming so close to them that they consider you one of the group," Owen wrote Hardy. "Soon you join their 'gab fests'—soon you begin to get to them by example, by implication, by precept, those things that can build character. Soon you are their leader. Soon they are just like so much clay in your hands to be molded." Perhaps, Owen wrote, Hardy might one day live with the Hardy Scholars themselves. "But I do not want to spend any money on buildings or bricks or mortar," Owen wrote. "I want to spend it on creating that intangible 'something' which after all is the heart of everything."

Owen was determined to improve the moral standards at the university. "I have learned to know considerable in the last three years about two things at Northwestern: (1) the athletic department, and (2) the fraternity houses. Both need a great deal of transformation," he wrote. "Morals at Northwestern, like many schools, do not seem to exist among as many of the students as should be the case."

On January 17, 1935, Hardy responded with a six-page letter in which he told Owen that he was making a good decision by not erecting "brick and mortar" memorials. "Too many people look upon a college or a university in terms of buildings, laboratories, stadium, or beautiful grounds," Hardy wrote. "These are good—some of them are necessary—but the test lies at the point of what is done to the mind and the character of the student who spends four years on the campus."

Hardy believed that the first challenge would be picking the right scholars. "A first-class product can hardly come from second- and third-rate raw material," he wrote. Coon and Hardy needed to find above-average students who were earnest, honest, healthy, and possessed a good personality. To find the right scholars, Hardy suggested that they carefully study intelligence tests and high school records. But, he wrote, it is important to look beyond the exterior of students in order to find students with a set of principles on moral matters. High intelligence is not the key, he wrote. There is no point in trying to guide geniuses. "If the man be a real 'genius' he will do what he will do in spite of what course of treatment he gets, not because of it," Hardy wrote.

Soon after their arrival on the Northwestern campus, the Hardy scholars would take part in frequent meetings for discussion and criticism, Hardy wrote, but he warned Owen that they must go easy on the students. "No man can or ought to try to mold men as if they were putty—that can't be done," Hardy wrote. "While I remain, and am active, for example, I should expect to have these individuals meet me at my home for group discussions of all sorts of topics of interest to us. Here would be a chance for a good deal of give-and-take, out of which ought to come both correction of limitations and group solidarity in growth."

Hardy suggested to Owen that the pair not "ballyhoo" the scholarship program. Hardy was convinced that the mere announcement of the program would attract the proper number of applicants. Loud and long publicity was not educationally sound. "Such action may do harm, and be something of a handicap right at the start," Hardy wrote. "To make such a group 'special' so as to fasten a special classification to them on the campus has its dangers—dangers, first, to the individuals, and, second, to their human attachments with their fellows. Our man must be a human being who can influence others. To do so he must know others. To learn human motives and limitations requires mingling with all types on a common basis." He concluded: "Of one thing you may rest assured. My conviction is that you are starting a great idea. My heart is in it. I could ask for nothing better to work on. Everything I can give shall be given to make the project a success at once and continuously."

Two days later, Owen replied, saying that he agreed with Hardy. "As far as I am concerned, there are no restrictions from me or final suggestions given to you in any shape or manner," he wrote Hardy. Owen wrote that he expected Northwestern to give Hardy a free hand in choosing the scholars and running the program. "My end of the job is simple—simply work hard and make money, some of which you are to spend. As to whether you accomplish results and are a good spender—is your worry." Owen was clear that he expected success. "I trust you will pardon me the privilege, being strictly a business man and not a professional man—in wanting and demanding results from the expenditure of money."

After the exchange of letters, Owen changed his will to provide that 20 percent of his estate would be left for the scholarships. At present, he wrote, the amount would be about $100,000. "If I live another ten to fifteen years, it should be considerably more." Specifically, Owen wrote Thomas Gonser on January 21, 1935, that his new will called for $2,400 a year be paid to Northwestern University out of principal. After the death of his wife, 20 percent of his estate was to be paid directly to Northwestern University to be used for Hardy Scholars. Owen added that payment of scholarships should go uninterrupted after his death. But he demanded that Hardy be left alone to run the program properly. "I hope that administrative red tape and alumni pressure of a wrong description on behalf of a scholarship for this boy

63

or that boy may not be exercised upon Hardy, and I hope that he is given a free rein to develop the idea in a satisfactory manner." Owen warned the university that he might change his will if the program was not productive, or if Northwestern University started putting pressure on Hardy.

"I am not looking to Northwestern University as an institution to accomplish proper results from the expenditure of some money that I have made," Owen wrote. "I am looking exclusively to one Clarion DeWitt Hardy to get those results. I am looking to Clarion DeWitt Hardy to see that even his successor is trained so that proper results will follow, even after you have passed on."

Owen told Hardy to stick to his own high standards and not admit any unworthy candidates into the scholarship program. "Will you pardon me, therefore, as I know you will, for wanting to definitely fix the responsibility upon you and you alone." Owen wrote. "Whatever you say, whatever you do is O.K. and satisfactory with me. No criticism on anything you may do will ever be forthcoming from me, except when the percentage of failure becomes too high in the development of the recipients of these scholarships."

The exchange of letters between Coon and Hardy at the end of 1934 and the start of 1935 was the blueprint for the Hardy Scholarships. The key to making the program work was to let Hardy work without interference. Owen promised Hardy that he himself would not pressure Hardy or overly influence him.

"As I see the proper results being accomplished, I naturally will want to give more and more along the same line and to accomplish the same purpose—as proper results are obtained," Owen wrote. "There are no restrictions as far as I am concerned placed on the granting of such scholarships in any manner, shape, or form. When I look at the records of such boys at the end of one year, two years, three years, four years, and even longer thereafter—then I will know whether the proper results are being obtained."

CHAPTER FOUR

# The Scholars

---

"IF THE GOVERNMENT THINKS THAT WE FOUR FELLOWS
DON'T PUT IN HOURS OF WORK AND PLENTY OF THEM,
JUST LET THEM FOLLOW OUR PACE FOR A MONTH AND
WATCH THE NUMBER OF HOURS OF WORK WE PUT IN,
AND SEE HOW FEW PEOPLE THERE ARE IN THIS WORLD
THAT WOULD WANT TO FOLLOW A SIMILAR PACE AND
THE SACRIFICE OF HOME LIFE AND SOME OF THE PLEA-
SURES THAT OTHER PEOPLE GET."

The Clarion DeWitt Hardy Scholarships in Forensics were announced in May 1935. "It is my hope that these scholarships will bring serious minded students under the beneficent supervision of Professor Hardy and other members of the faculty of Northwestern University, and will enter them upon a course of training in forensics which I deem to be of most significant value in preparing for leadership in business or in public life," Owen Coon wrote. "I hope that these scholarships will attract to Northwestern University high-minded, promising young men."

Coon and Hardy communicated often during 1935 as they set up the grant program. Owen did not expect that the scholarships would change the world, but he did think they would help create students with powerful skills able to create a better world. "If they are just reasonably good scholars, within the top quarter of their University class," he wrote, "but with some trained ability in the expression of ideas, they will have marked influence in whatever kind of work they may take up at a later date."

About forty-five students applied for the Hardy Scholarships. Hardy, after some consultation with Coon, chose eight scholars for the 1935-36 school year. The process was not easy, Hardy wrote, because he was seeking candidates who showed as much leadership capability as academic prowess.

The scholars were:

—William Babcock, of Evanston. Babcock's father was a successful architect during the days of prosperity, Hardy wrote, but the family lost much of its fortune "after the big wind," a reference to the 1929 stock market crash. Babcock's high school teachers spoke highly of him, and Babcock handled himself well in the interview. "One of the reasons I was interested in Babcock was because he appears to come from a family that has a good deal of ability," Hardy wrote. Babcock went on to receive his bachelor's degree in business administration from Northwestern and higher degrees from the University of Wisconsin and Columbia University. He retired as an executive with the Bank of America.

—John E. Fobes, of Chicago. He was a high-ranking student and leader in high school. "I think he promises well," Hardy wrote. Fobes graduated from Northwestern with a bachelor's degree in political science, earned a master's degree from Tufts University, and became a professor.

—Page Procter Jr., of Bloomington, Illinois. He came to Northwestern with a fine high school record as a good scholar. He was the only candidate not interviewed by Hardy, but had impeccable credentials. Graduating from Northwestern with honors, he went on to earn a master's degree and doctorate from Yale University. He became an executive with the New York advertising firm of J. Walter Thompson.

—James A. Rahl, of Wooster, Ohio. Rahl was "a tall, angular boy, reaching, I should say, about six feet four inches in height," Hardy wrote. Rahl ranked second in his high school class of 172, was president of the senior class, and participated on the debate team. Hardy met his father and was impressed with him as a "first-class, honest type of citizen." Hardy's only concern was with Rahl's appearance. "The boy does have an infection or eruptions on his face, which rather mar his appearance, but I am told that usually this kind of trouble is a matter of youth—he is only seventeen years old—and that probably his difficulty will disappear with a little more maturity." Rahl graduated from the School of Speech in 1939 and went directly to Northwestern Law School, where he graduated first in his class. He become a national authority on antitrust law and was a member of the law school faculty from 1946 to 1994, serving as dean from 1972 to 1977.

—Lewis H. Sarett Jr., of Ravinia, Illinois. A top student at Deerfield-Shields High School in Highland Park, Sarett was earnest,

66

ambitious, and eager to get ahead, Hardy wrote. His father, Lewis Sarett Sr., was a speech professor at Northwestern. "Unless I am mistaken, he is a young man that we will all hear about some day," Hardy wrote. "I rather think his main interest will be in scientific studies, although it is perhaps too early to be right sure about that." Sarett was selected because of his "very superior ability and promise."

Sarett became an organic chemist. In 1944, working for Merck & Company, he developed the first synthetic version of cortisone. Four years later, the drug was proven to be effective in the treatment of rheumatoid arthritis. During his thirty-eight years at Merck, Sarett was named as the primary inventor or collaborator on 100 technical papers and patents. He received the American Chemical Society Award for Creative Chemistry in 1964 and was elected to the National Inventors Hall of Fame. In 1976, President Gerald Ford awarded Sarett the National Medal of Science, the nation's highest award for academic achievement. He died in 1999.

—Paul F. Schwaighart Jr., of Midlothian, Illinois. Schwaighart was "a likable young man" near the top of his class, Hardy wrote. The student had scored high on intelligence tests and was involved in many student activities. Schwaighart graduated from the School of Commerce and became a certified public accountant. He worked as a partner in an accounting firm.

—Gloria Rensch, of Evanston. She was a graduate of Evanston Township High School and had a special aptitude for foreign languages, English, and art. She was a "very agreeable young woman," Hardy wrote, one of four or five women who had applied for scholarships, and "the one lady that I have chosen." Hardy was impressed with her father, a former businessman who had lost his high-paying job during the Depression, but continued to work as a salesman. The father, Hardy wrote, is "a man of personality and good parts. The same can be said of the mother. The daughter has good stock in her." Rensch graduated with a bachelor's degree and master's degree in classics and worked much of her career at the Terre Haute, Indiana, public library. She died in 2001.

—Horace Howells, of Corvallis, Oregon, was the final Hardy Scholar. He replaced a student who had dropped out of school after his first freshman days because of a death in the family. Howells had managed to get a job at Hill's Restaurant and at the Marshall Field's store during the first weeks of his freshman year. "In his case, I am quite convinced that we have a find," Hardy wrote. He said the student is "straight, neat, clean," talks well, and "gives promise of unusual development." Ironically, Howells was the only original Hardy scholar to fail to graduate. Even with the full scholarship and both jobs, he couldn't make ends meet. He married in 1938, enlisted in the Navy, and later founded the successful Howells Department Store in Newport, Oregon. He died in 1998.

‡    ‡    ‡    ‡

HARDY WROTE TO COON at the start of the year that he hoped to bring all the scholars together to introduce themselves and discuss the purposes of college. Hardy served as the advisor to the two scholars in the School of Speech. The other six, all in the College of Liberal Arts, had other advisors. Nonetheless, Hardy met frequently with all the scholars. Owen and Louise entertained them several times in an attempt to infuse them with the ideas behind the scholarship. "I have no doubt about the basic capacity of these young people to be successful in college," Hardy wrote. "The one anxiety that I do have is as to whether we can keep them from getting sidetracked into too many things so that their industry, so far as their job is concerned, may be affected. That is, of course, part of my job."

Hardy knew it would take several years to get results, but he was confident. "I shall assure you I shall be a much disappointed man if I cannot make this venture a success," he wrote to Owen. Hardy's goal was to produce students who could productively serve business and the community. He wrote: "You know, friend Coon, if in education we can't make better men and better women, then what is education for? Scholarship, as such, has never appealed very much to me, particularly in a country like ours. What America needs today more than anything else is more people with wisdom and judgment, common sense, balance, industry, and capacity to work."

Owen agreed. Rather than teach cold hard facts that might soon be forgotten, professors should understand the importance of teaching good morals, proper business ethics and social responsibility. "University training can have too much 'doctor of philosophy' business in it to suit me," he wrote. "When all university professors realize that a lot of the education they have to pass on to boys and girls is not in the books they teach, far greater results will be obtained."

In September 1935, Owen sent the first check of $1,200 to Northwestern. "I trust that the seven boys and one girl that have been selected are good specimens of humanity and I trust that they will 'Go Places,'" Owen wrote Northwestern's Thomas Gonser. In February 1936, Hardy sent a handwritten letter to "My Dear Owen," detailing the academic progress of the eight scholars. "The record of our scholars for the first semester is a creditable one in my judgment," Hardy assured his benefactor. The average grade was an A- and the average score was a 5.78. (The Northwestern University scale during those years was 7 for an A, 6 for an A-, 5 for a B+, etc.) The eight scholars received only a few Bs and one C.

"If we can keep up this record, or something like it—your money will be well invested—that is, if money can be well placed anywhere for a man except under his own supervision," Hardy wrote. "Our world is filled with so much waste of time, energy and money, that I don't want to be a party to wasting any more—especially when the money belongs to another." He signed his note: "Sincerely yours as ever/Hardy."

Owen was pleased. He wrote to Hardy that his only concern was whether the scholars were receiving proper training in forensics. He hoped that most of the scholars would become members of Delta Sigma Rho, the honorary debating fraternity, because that would prove they had the ability to express their ideas and make their influence felt. "I am having one or two of the fellows come down and see me each Saturday afternoon when I am in town so that I can gradually become better acquainted with them, and this fellow Howells you can tell for me, he has a job when he gets through school, if he keeps on going like he is now." In April 1936, Owen wrote that he would expand the program to make ten scholarships available to students for the 1936-37 school year. All eight of the original scholarships were renewed.

But in the summer of 1936, everything suddenly and unexpectedly changed. Clarion DeWitt Hardy contracted a streptococcus infection and died. He was only fifty-eight. "Although Professor Hardy had been ill for a year, it was not generally known that his condition was serious," reported the *Evanston News Index*. "He was taken to the hospital about two weeks ago when he steadily grew worse." Attorney Dean Traxler wrote to Owen: "We all grieved at noting in yesterday's *Tribune* the untimely death of Professor Clarion DeWitt Hardy on June 27th."

Hardy's death, Traxler wrote, meant that Owen's will would have to be modified. The will specified that the Hardy Scholarships committee would be comprised of the Northwestern president, the School of Speech director of personnel and Hardy and his designated successor, but no successor had been named. Traxler suggested the fifth member of the committee be the dean of the Northwestern School of Speech.

Owen had little time to reflect. He left the country on a scheduled trip to Europe. The following month, he made it clear that he still supported the scholarship program. He signed a new will, which stipulated that upon his death his wife would pay Northwestern University $3,000 per year to support the Hardy Scholarships.

Hardy left behind his wife, two grown sons, and a daughter who had just graduated from high school. Owen wrote Gonser in September 1936 that he wanted to help pay the tuition at Northwestern for Hardy's daughter, Mary Louise. The university paid half and Owen paid the other half. He wanted nobody to know about his generosity. Mary Louise did not graduate from Northwestern. She married Dean Smith, who years later would become president of Sears Roebuck.

After Hardy's death, Owen realized he should be more specific in outlining the general requirements for Hardy Scholars. In early 1937, he wrote Gonser that he wanted sufficient speech training for Hardy Scholars. "I want these students to know how to organize a speech, how to write one, how to give it—and without having to read it from a piece of paper when it is delivered. (If there was anything I learned from Clarion DeWitt Hardy, it was to never read a speech—but if such had to be done, never to give it.)" Gonser replied two days later that Owen's ideas about a rigid speech requirement were not appropriate for all Hardy Scholars.

"It is my opinion that to commit yourself and the prospective Hardy-Coon scholars to the necessity of taking any specific course in any school would detract from a certain elasticity of the educational program which you have in mind and which I am sure you wish to preserve," Gonser wrote. Owen was not satisfied with this response. He wrote to Northwestern President Walter Dill Scott in April 1937 that he wanted Hardy Scholars to take twenty-five hours of speech education (about 20 percent of their courses) and a minimum of six hours each year, beginning with the next school year. He also insisted that each scholar participate in one public university debate or oratorical contest each year.

"Such scholars were told at the beginning of this year that participation in debate and oratorical work was necessary, and I feel that this scholarship should be revoked as to such scholars that have not followed this suggestion during the current year," Owen wrote. "Otherwise, I am simply assisting in the creation of excellent scholars who will not have the ability to properly 'sell' to others the ideas they originate later in life."

Owen was chagrined that his Hardy Scholars outside the School of Speech were finding it nearly impossible to schedule twenty hours of speech education during their four years at Northwestern. "I have no real desire to have these Hardy Scholars segregated into the School of Speech," he wrote. But he was distressed that the university was not flexible enough to adopt his suggested speech requirements. "Such a restriction I will not accept—and pay the bill!" he wrote.

In 1937, Owen openly criticized the Northwestern bureaucracy and the autonomy each department possessed. "As you know, my heart and soul has been with Northwestern University," he wrote President Scott. "From what I am beginning to find out, however, its education set up is apparently so antiquated and so in the hands of numerous deans, one pulling this way and another pulling another way, that it is a serious question in my mind as to whether an individual like myself, who desires to see (whether rightly or wrongly) a certain degree of emphasis placed on a certain type of education should not go elsewhere than at Northwestern to have such a result accomplished."

Scott's response, which is not to be found among Coon's papers, must have been frustrating to Owen. "I have written and torn up three different letters—one of them five pages in length," he wrote back to Scott. "In reply, I wish only to state that the scholarships I thought to establish were to be called the 'Hardy Scholarships in Forensics,' not just scholarships alone."

The only restriction Owen had ever placed on his scholarship proposal was that students be given a satisfactory education in speech. "My letter of April 8th was written only when I found Northwestern University was not living up to its implied contract with me, as a donor of these scholarships," Owen wrote. "Much to my surprise, I find that some of them, while excellent students, have never even so much as had a single course in speech education, much less have they been required to engage in any kind of debate or oratorical training work—all as clearly requested in my original letter establishing these scholarships."

After a conversation with Addison Hibbard, dean of Northwestern's College of Liberal Arts, Owen was so upset that he told President Scott he was rethinking his commitment to the scholarship program. "I think perhaps Dean Hibbard is correct in that it is not up to an ordinary businessman to lay down picayune restrictions as to how a certain type of educational program is to be developed. I agree that I am not an expert along these lines. I know, however, the result that I expect to have attained by the university—or my future interests along this line will not continue."

Owen was specific, threatening to rewrite his will if the university did not require debate and public speaking training for Hardy Scholars. "In the meantime, I am withdrawing any suggestion as to how the proper result is to be obtained, and will await the receipt of a detailed program to be submitted by the university as to how and in what manner I can be assured that what the university was to do—will be done. ...Failing to receive proper assurances as to how the purposes of these scholarships are to be carried out, from the university administration, I shall change my will and establish the scholarships elsewhere."

‡    ‡    ‡    ‡

By 1937, General Finance operated out of seven offices in Michigan and Illinois. By then, Owen and his family owned or controlled 300,000 shares of the corporation's stock, worth about $675,000. The company made $18 million in loans in 1938 and reported a net income of $163,960 for the fiscal year. It handled $34 million in loans in 1939 and reported a net income of $339,000. In addition to making loans, the company organized the Mid-America Insurance Company, a profitable arm of General Finance that offered insurance on borrowers' cars. The company's name later was changed to Mid-States Insurance Company.

Success, of course, did not come without long hours of intense work. Owen described how hard he and his three top employees worked in a 1936 letter to accountant Harry Baumann. Owen wrote the letter as part of preparations for a defense to challenges by the Internal Revenue Service. The letter, and documents prepared by his attorneys for the IRS audit, give an inside look at the early years of General Finance. Owen wrote:

> I have been constantly engaged in this line of work
> for the last eleven years, and during such period

have always worked four nights a week in addition to Sunday afternoons in 50 percent of the cases, together with a shift from 8:30 in the morning until 6 in the afternoon, not including the night work above mentioned. I understand that you want this information for government tax purposes. If the government does not think this is the case, let them put an agent on my trail and let him follow me sight unseen for a month, and then if any government man wants to take my place, and wants to lead the same kind of a pace that I have had to lead whether I wanted to or not, he is certainly welcome to do so.

I have to spend 50 percent of my time away from home, making a round trip each week to Detroit, one day a week in Pontiac, one day a week in Waukegan, in addition to all the regular routine work of calling on banks, dealers, handling office work in an automobile as I go from place to place, or else at night after everyone has gone home, except my brother, Lyle Titus and Ray Titus.

Owen wrote that Byron, who had joined the business in 1928, handled all the collection work, supervised the company's Chicago division and wholesale financing. "It is seldom that he works less than three evenings a week, in addition to the daytime schedule of between nine and ten hours daily—six days a week, with two weeks off each year for a vacation," Owen wrote.

Another of Byron's responsibilities was to take back cars if a dealership liquidated. "Due to Byron S. Coon's ability and careful supervision of these transactions, the company has, in every case, realized payment of its claims in full, together with reimbursement for expenses," wrote Richard Oldberg, attorney for the company.

Lyle A. Titus, who formerly worked as a cashier in a bank in Baraboo, Wisconsin, began working for Motor Acceptance in 1926. He served principally as the credit manager, supervising the purchase of each retail deal by the company. "His duties require knowledge of the value of all models of all automobiles manufactured during the preceding five-year period, so that he can determine how much the company can invest in each transaction," wrote attorney Oldberg. "He is also required to be familiar with the rates offered by the numerous competitors."

Ray E. Titus, who joined the company in 1928, was in charge of the company's repossessed car department. He reconditioned and resold the cars. Ray worked the hardest of all Motor Acceptance Company employees. "Without his sales ability and without his knowledge of knowing what cars to repair and what cars not to have repaired and how much to spend on each one of them in the reconditioning, our company would have such losses as would make its existence impossible," Owen wrote.

That left Owen to fill in the gaps. "My job is to get the money from banks and help get the business from dealers, and to do everything else in between that nobody else does," he wrote. "If the government thinks that we four fellows don't put in hours of work and plenty of them, just let them follow our pace for a month and watch the number of hours of work we put in, and see how few people there are in this world that would want to follow a similar pace and the sacrifice of home life and some of the pleasures that other people get. In other words, frankly I am about sick of the pace we lead anyway."

‡    ‡    ‡    ‡

CREDIT CAME TO BE an integral part of American life during the 1930s and auto finance companies led the way, according to *Time* magazine. "Following in the footsteps of the successful car financiers, products of almost every kind and description are now sold in installment," the magazine reported. But the trend had ominous overtones. *Time* warned, "To conservative economists this vast expansion and its simultaneous easing of credit—to the point of no down payments and up to five years to pay—has begun to look like a tremendously top-heavy inflation which might well play the same lead in the next depression that overextended Wall Street credit played in the last."

Car credit companies changed dramatically during the 1930s. The government began tighter scrutiny of sales finance firms and the industry developed a distinctly poor reputation among the public. "When Herbert Hoover moved out of the White House and Franklin D. Roosevelt moved in, a new economic era emerged in this country," Owen wrote in the *Texas Association of Automobile Finance Companies News Bulletin.* "As we all know, the first important development of this new age was the growth of governmental regulation and interference or participation in business. We had some of it before, but certainly what we have had since 1933 is far more important and extensive than what we ever had before."

Both state and local government began taking a closer look at the industry. "Things which finance companies formerly did which were thought perfectly fitting and proper have come into disrepute," Owen wrote. "Things that I formerly did in the operation of my business which were perfectly proper at the time now make my conscience hurt when I look back upon them. Such is again a development of this new economic era. You just must do things differently today than you did ten or twelve years ago!"

During the 1930s, Owen started to look beyond financing cars. He was determined to play a leading role in reforming the auto loan industry, and became a force behind the American Finance Conference, formed in 1933 to unify and upgrade the industry. Coon was appointed president of the group in November 1937 and was re-elected in 1938. He was a frequent speaker at its annual convention.

Always practical, Owen suggested that finance companies work within the new government rules. "Accept the regulation as a group and try to steer it into helpful channels," he wrote. "Don't try to fight it, because if you do, you are only bucking a trend. One makes money in this country by floating with the trend and trying to direct and shape it and not trying to buck it."

But Owen urged finance companies to band together to resist further government interference, just as finance companies had jointly fought the proposed rules and regulations of the National Recovery Act's Code Authority. "If you want to protect your business you must do it in pressure groups," he wrote. "I well remember in the fall of 1933 when the first committee went to Washington in the code fight. The committees reported back to a group of us that they were told in Washington that if a sizable section of our industry does not like certain things in the code they should make themselves heard." The industry, Owen wrote, was successful in shaping the new code.

An even greater problem, Owen wrote, was the tarnished reputation that burdened car credit companies. "You recall that it hasn't been so very long ago that stock brokers were 'on the pan,' then the bankers, next the public utility men, and now it seems our turn has come," Owen wrote. The criticism was unwarranted, he wrote, but needed to be addressed. "Our business is not one-tenth as bad as some people are trying to paint it," he wrote. "I doubt if our business has as many things wrong with it ethically as have most of the other businesses in this country."

Owen suggested that credit companies revise their business practices to improve their image. They should "bend over backwards" to make friends among their clientele. "Do what the public wants and you will take the kick out of criticism of our industry," he wrote. "The trend very distinctly today is to protect the customer more. Sit up nights thinking how you can give such protection—how you can take the complaints out of your business, and how you can inspire confidence on the part of the public to want to do business with a finance company instead of through an automobile club and a bank."

‡    ‡    ‡    ‡

THE INTERNAL REVENUE SERVICE challenged almost every tax return Owen Coon filed in the 1930s. Some of these disputes were small; others required a great deal of Owen's attention. The IRS questioned the substantial bonuses paid to Motor Acceptance Company officers in the early 1930s, but those challenges were settled for a few thousand dollars.

The more vexing and costly tax dispute arose from the merger of General Finance and Motor Acceptance Company in 1935. In the late 1930s, the IRS charged General Finance with an extra $211,000 in tax liability plus $76,000 in interest for a total of $287,000. The government argued that Owen and other officers of Motor Acceptance had not fully reported gains from the merger. Owen contested the government's claim, contending there had been no taxable gain.

Initially, the government agreed with Owen. "After consideration of the material facts, the IRS in Chicago accepted the return as filed and did not recommend any increase in the value of shares," wrote attorney Oldberg. The IRS reversed itself in 1938, however, concluding that Owen had profited greatly from the merger and had not reported his profit.

Many of Owen's business associates came to his defense as he prepared to rebute the government's claims. They wrote letters to the IRS in support of his argument that General Finance was not worth a great deal of money at the time of the merger. "What the company need-ed was working capital and it was a most fortunate circumstance that a plan was devised in November and December of 1935 which resulted in the sale of $750,000 debentures subordinated as to the company's bank loans," wrote Charles A. Parcells, who ran the Parcells investment firm. "Without this particularly fortunate piece of financing, the company would not have had the opportunity of growth and consequent larger earnings for the common stock which subsequently made the company's stock more valuable and which value was reflected in its market."

Resolution of the dispute extended for several years. The pri-mary question was the fair market value of 390,000 shares of common stock that General Finance Corporation issued in the transaction with Coon's Motor Acceptance Company. In 1938, Internal Revenue agents determined that General Finance preferred stock had been worth $10 per share and common stock worth $4 per share at the time of the merger. Owen's lawyers argued that the common shares should be valued at $1.18 per share. The government finally agreed in 1942 to settle the matter for a sum of $25,000, plus $9,000 in interest. "After arriving at a tentative settlement with the government on the above outlined basis, we recommend that it be adopted," Oldberg wrote Owen. "Our legal defenses are extremely technical and without precedent except by analogy, and that upon trying the factual side of the case we could hardly expect to drive the value of General Finance common stock below $2.50 to $3 a share."

Oldberg wrote that he felt their chances of winning the case on the merits of the legal arguments were perhaps 10 to 15 per cent. Owen agreed to the settlement offer in June 1942 to eliminate continued litiga-tion. But the dispute left Owen in a financial bind. In 1942, he asked the IRS that he be allowed to pay off his remaining balance at a rate of $1,000 a month. He explained that his company was going through difficult times because of the war. "It is most essential that my credit reputation be maintained, as the credit of General Finance Corporation has largely been secured as a result of my efforts and support, and the fact I have kept a perfect credit reputation personally during all this period of time," he wrote.

The additional tax bill, he wrote, was the result of a techni-cal legal question that still remained unanswered. No additional taxes would have been demanded had the merger been handled differently, he argued. "I have always paid my bill, and will continue to do so," he continued. "This is the first time in my life I have been unable to meet any obligation on the day it was due. I have always kept my finances under control, my debts paid, my credit reputation clear. The reason for the privilege of paying the above mentioned tax in monthly installments arises solely as a result of a desire on the part of myself, as well as the government, to settle a tax controversy at this time, creating an immediate liability."

He later wrote: "I am paying 6 percent interest on the deferred balance, and naturally will try to hasten the liquidation of my other obligations as fast as possible in order that I can make some loan arrangements in due course on a cheaper basis than this, which would enable me at that time to pay off the obligation in full. At the present time, however, it is just simply impossible for me to pay more than $1,000 a month on the principal and interest of the taxes due from me, after cleaning up all the interest secured to date, without tearing down the credit structure which I have been most careful to build."

Coon's request was accepted.

‡      ‡      ‡      ‡

DESPITE HIS THREATENING LETTERS to Northwestern officials, Owen continued his support of the Hardy Scholarships program, and the administration apparently complied with his demand that Hardy Scholars be required to take more speech and debate training. In 1937, Owen wrote to Ralph Dennis, dean of the School of Speech, that he was satisfied with Dennis's plan. "The restrictions which you have outlined for the educational development of the Hardy Scholars as the result of our recent conversation is most agreeable to me," Owen wrote, "and if followed will fulfill in perfect fashion all of the thoughts I have had in connection with this matter."

Owen was so satisfied with this new codification of the Hardy Scholarships that he was content to write only a few letters to Northwestern during the 1937-38 and 1938-39 school years. University officials kept him informed about the scholars—their names, academic standing and progress in forensics. The Hardy Scholars averaged a grade of 6.11 on the 7-point scale during the 1938-39 school year, the highest group average achieved by Hardy Scholars during that era.

In June 1939, Coon decided to donate money to build a lounge for Hardy Scholars in Scott Hall, the new student union building on campus. He wanted the new facility to be a place where students and teachers would gather. He saw it as a hangout for "bull sessions" and discussions, lectures, informal or practice debates, and speakers. Owen's wife, Louise, took over the planning of the room. "You have now got into the realm, however, of things which my wife has far more knowledge and experience in than do I," Owen wrote Clarence T. Simon, who had taken over from Dennis as acting dean of the School of Speech.

Simon suggested that the room be equipped with built-in bookcases for magazines and books. Owen also wanted the bookcases to hold essays and debates of Hardy Scholars as well as a record detailing the future achievements of Hardy Scholars. The room would have a wood-burning fireplace with easy chairs, ashtrays and reading lamps, a radio or radio-Victrola combination with good musical recordings, transcriptions of famous speeches, and a conference table. The key was to build relationships among students and the faculty. "If you get the right kind of student and the right kind of a professor together, it does not make much difference what the curriculum might be—the proper end will be achieved," Owen wrote. "Too many professors never realize this. The lounge will be a failure unless that idea is stressed in some form to whomever enters it."

By 1939, it appeared that the Hardy Scholarships were bearing fruit. Students such as Gloria Rensch and James Rahl sent Owen letters testifying to how the program had improved their lives. Wrote Gonser: "You and Louise certainly must get a great deal of satisfaction from the expressions of individuals who are not only getting the opportunity for their education but are having the opportunity to work for a specific purpose, a goal which of necessity means success. I hope that in some way the friendly spirit which exists between the students, faculty, and yourself will continue forever."

Gonser suggested that the letters to Coon be kept in the Hardy archives, but Owen disagreed. "I am afraid that putting these letters written to me personally, in any kind of permanent form, is going to make too much of personal publicity for myself, a thing which I do not relish," he wrote. "I have always thought that too much publicity of such acts on the part of donors only cheapens what they hope to do." Late in the year, Owen sent three more testimonials to the "secret file."

Owen, feeling like a parent to these students, wrote: "It is going to be a lot of fun in future years, seeing these boys and girls grow up, get interested in various lines of activity—makes success out of what they attempt to do." One of the scholars, Peggy Dunn, had recently married a Northwestern professor. "Believe me, she is sure a go-getter!" Owen wrote. "Unless I miss my guess, the wives of University men within the next ten years will very much know she is around." Peggy Dunn Brogan went on to pursue a doctorate in education, write three books, teach at the Home School in New York City and serve as an educational consultant. Her 1988 *New York Times* death notice said she "leaves behind thousands of children who were touched by her work."

In May 1940, Owen wrote that he wanted to expand the scholarship program to twenty students, five in each undergraduate class. "Once upon a time you sent me a book called *Investment for Eternity*," Owen wrote to Gonser. "How true that is. Two weeks after I am dead and gone anything else that I may have done in my short span of years will be forgotten about. Perhaps this one project in which I have become interested will be the only thing which I will leave after me, which will be of any permanent lasting value. It is certainly an investment that is paying far more than 6 percent per annum dividends."

Gonser replied that Hardy would be especially pleased with the 1939-40 Hardy Scholars, because they have "proved outstanding." He wrote: "Your pleasure will doubtless increase with the years, for these boys cannot help but make good for themselves in life after the grand start they have made. And that start, in good measure, they owe to you.

"Although I cannot agree that your achievements in the business world will be forgotten for a long, long time," Gonser wrote. "I do believe that each new Hardy Scholar will renew your memory and vitalize your name perpetually through their splendid records."

By the start of the school year, the Hardy Lounge was open.

"I have heard several persons say that in their opinion the Hardy Lounge in Scott Hall was one of the most attractive and distinctive rooms in the entire building," wrote Gonser. Owen was pleased, and added a few final touches to the room, including a framed scroll that read: "Give me a log hut, with only a simple bench, Mark Hopkins on one end and I on the other, and you may have all the buildings, apparatus, and libraries without him." This was a famous 1871 quote from President James A. Garfield talking about his Williams College teacher Mark

Hopkins. Owen was impressed with the Hardy Scholars graduating class in 1940-41. He wrote Dean Ralph Dennis in 1941 that he was proud to award Hardy medals to the eight graduates on Alumni Day.

But things changed after the start of World War II. The war, of course, had a profound impact on the Hardy Scholarships program. Thirteen scholars left Northwestern during the war to serve in the military. One Hardy graduate, Harald Christopher, was killed at Pearl Harbor on December 7, 1941. Christopher, who had started at Northwestern in 1937, was on the debate team and graduated in the School of Speech in June 1941. He was the first alumnus to give his life in the war.

The war also tended to reduce the high academic achievements of the Hardy Scholars. "The grade averages are a distinct disappointment to me and I have mentioned that fact in no uncertain terms to all of the offenders," wrote Clarence Simon, of the School of Speech. "In view of the uncertainty ahead of these boys and their general recklessness, this drop in grades is quite understandable. But I think we should make every effort to keep them at the highest level in spite of circumstances."

From 1935 until 1943, a total of forty-seven people were awarded the Hardy Scholarships. Four graduated with highest distinction and nine graduated with distinction. The first graduates received bronze Hardy medals upon graduation, but rationing made it impossible to use that metal during the war. To find worthy students during the war, Simon subscribed to a press-clipping bureau that sent him news of high school debate tournaments. He sent out more than 100 letters to these contest winners to recruit top scholars. The recruitment letters went like this:

> Congratulations to you and your teammates on your sweepstakes winning in the Nebraska District Tournament of the National Forensic League. They turn out good speakers in the State of Nebraska, and a win in this type of competition is something to bring definite pleasure.

Or like this:

> I have just heard of your participation in the Los Angeles tryouts for the Jefferson Memorial Ora-

torical Contest. I am sure you must have enjoyed competing with your fellow speakers in this hotly contested section of this large contest.

To maintain high academic standards, Northwestern also began offering high school juniors a chance to register for accelerated programs during the war. After their junior year, the high school students were allowed to take summer classes in Evanston. If successful, they could skip their fourth year in high school and start as full-time college students. Hardy Scholarships were made available to these young Northwestern students if they were deserving.

The letters from prospective candidates tell of the difficult clash between academics and military duty during the war years. James Forney, of Chicago, wrote in 1943: "I should like to take advantage of your accelerated program starting with the summer semester in order that I might complete one full year of college work before my assignment to duty as a Naval Aviation Cadet, which will follow my eighteenth birthday next December. I have recently completed my enlistment process in the Naval V-5 program, for reserve cadets to be assigned to Navy pilot training."

James Gammon responded to a Hardy solicitation, "It has been my desire for several years to attend the United States Naval Academy. In light of present circumstances, I feel this achievement is even more to be desired." In a similar fashion, John F. Monroe Jr. wrote, "I appreciate your informing me of the scholarship opportunities of Northwestern, Dr. Simon, but I was appointed to the Virginia Military Institute about two months ago, and due to world conditions, my parents wish me to proceed with my plans to attend V.M.I."

Other letters stressed the inevitability of the military draft. John C. Langley, of San Antonio, Texas, wrote, "Were it not that I have taken the Army A12 examination and expect to be inducted in the near future, I would be greatly interested in these scholarships to Northwestern." Marvin Levich, of Sioux City, Iowa, wrote, "I do appreciate the offer of a scholarship contained therein, but there are obstacles to my attending college at all. I am rapidly nearing the draft age, and will not graduate till next January. Whether I can go to college is still problematical."

Simon congratulated all of the men who planned to serve in the military. To Levich, for example, he wrote, "It may be possible that after this war is over and you find yourself in civilian clothes, you may wish to make plans to further your education. If that is the case, I should appreciate hearing from you at the time (if I am still on the job) and perhaps we can help you make some plans."

Simon wrote to a Minnesota prospect in 1943 explaining that most Hardy Scholarships were for 2/3 tuition, or $200 per year. "Evanston, like many other towns in these days, is suffering from a distinct labor shortage," Simon wrote. "Many homes, formerly well supplied with hired assistants, are now minus that help. Consequently, there are almost unlimited opportunities for an energetic man to add substantially to his income without too great interference with his academic career."

By the end of the 1943 school year, only seven Hardy Scholars, five men and two women, still were taking classes. And only five alumni still lived in the Chicago area. Wrote Coon: "Sentimentally, I should very much like to have a meeting of these Hardy Scholars in the old style. But practically, I know that is impossible. If the discussion last winter at the Orrington [Hotel] was somewhat dominated by faculty and previous Hardy Scholars, it would be much more so at this time."

Only two Hardy Scholarships were awarded in 1943—one to William C. Lantz of Sioux Falls, South Dakota, and one to Carolyn Anne Bennorth of Elgin, Illinois. Wrote Simon: "Your committee has not felt that it should grant a larger number of these scholarships to women students. . . . The one woman we have mentioned, however, is such an outstanding person and is definitely able in forensics that we feel justified in granting her this honor."

To record the legacy of these scholars, Owen spent $350 to complete the Book of the Hardy Scholars in 1943. The book was a lovely piece of art. It was 14-by-18 inches in size, bound in full wine-red Morocco leather, and tooled in gold leaf with an original design. "The Hardy Scholarship Book is a joy to all beholders," wrote Simon.

Owen had kept every scrap of publicity on his scholars and had to determine who exactly would be included in the book—any Hardy Scholars or only those who graduated. (Nine scholars from 1935 to 1941 failed to graduate.) And should he include the Hardy Scholars who failed to graduate because they joined the military? He first decided not to include them.

"If they return and graduate, they will be included in the book," he wrote in July 1943. "If by any chance they happen to be war casualties, I think they should be included, graduation or no. If, on the other hand, they simply peter out and either fail to return or returning fail to make the grade then I doubt that we should include them even though they have been members of the armed forces."

Three days later, Owen changed his mind. All Hardy Scholars who served in the armed forces, he now believed, should be included in the book. "The mere fact that a boy has had to drop out of school to enter the armed forces should not be held against him, whether or not he later returns to Northwestern, because conditions may have changed so as to make his final graduation next to impossible," Owen wrote.

The book was important to Owen because it captured the essence of the program's purpose and memorialized the scholars.

It concluded: "May their lives be an endless chain of service and inspiration to others."

# Chapter Five

# The War Changes Everything

"He was big on war drives. Mom and I would travel to Park Ridge and places like that to watch him give speeches. Everybody knew him or knew of him. I remember listening to a lot of speeches."

Owen and Louise Coon returned to Evanston in 1940. They bought a twenty-two room brick mansion at 1201 Sheridan Road for $57,500, far less than the $100,000 it cost to build in 1913. They made more than $10,000 in improvements to the house before moving in during the spring of 1940. Then Louise filled it with Chippendale furniture. "The family expressed its pleasure this week at the opportunity to return to Evanston civic and social activities," the *Evanston Review* noted. The Coons sold their Glencoe home at 150 Park Avenue for $25,000.

Owen focused most of his attention on work, Eleanor said. "He never had any time for any of us, and that included Louise. During the war, when he couldn't go to Europe on vacation, they would go to Mexico." But even in Mexico, he missed his business affairs. High in the mountains outside Mexico City, at a resort in San Jose Perua, he would wade through boxes of office papers while taking sulfur baths.

"He bought a bus company in Mexico City and then he was involved in building a hotel there," Eleanor said. Business opportunities were always around the corner. Owen sent Lyle Titus to Hawaii to look into a scrap metal factory and sent Ray Titus to Seattle to check out a factory making beef stew for GIs. Eleanor recalls that he invested $100,000 in a Hedy Lamarr movie. "Wherever he went, he was bored doing nothing. Then he would get busy and invest in something," she said. "Then he probably took the ticket off his taxes. I know my father."

Yet overall, when Owen did relax, it was on trips and holidays. Harry Coon and Owen Coon Jr. recall their father unwinding when he took them on his yacht. In the late 1930s, Owen's doctor ordered him to find a way to simmer down, so he bought the fifty-four-foot Sea Bee from an estate in Philadelphia. It was a beautiful boat with a black hull that rivaled Philip K. Wrigley's boat, its neighbor in Belmont Harbor. Owen hired a captain, a cook, and another sailor and sailed on Lake Michigan during the summer and off the coasts of Florida during the winter. Owen also enjoyed driving to Byron's summer hideout in Lac du Flambeau in the north woods of Wisconsin, where he fished, built fires, and cooked bacon. "What a beauty spot it is," he once wrote. "Beautiful lake, splendid swimming, nice Chris-Craft boat, etc."

Eleanor recalls how much her father loved the Christmas season. It was then, she said, that the whole family saw Owen as a generous, sentimental person. One year, he tied a gift for Louise to the end of a long string that wound through the house. "She had to follow the string to her emerald ring," Eleanor recalled. "We all watched and had so much fun. I thought it was sweet."

The couple showed their affection and loyalty in other ways, too. Owen and Louise were a devoted couple, Owen Jr. recalled. He would open doors for her and kiss her in public. "Owen could count on Louise," Eleanor said. "He knew she was home fixing dinner. She gave him a home." But by the mid-1940s, the couple sometimes bickered, often at odds with each other about the raising of their children. Harry said they even talked about divorce, but he is not certain how serious a possibility that ever became.

Owen and Louise took vacations—sometimes alone, sometimes with the family, and sometimes with friends. They took Rose Coon on a five-week tour of Germany, Denmark, Sweden, and Russia in the late 1930s, sailing from New York City on the SS *Bremen*. In 1940, they went on a ten-day motor trip to Washington, D.C., and White Sulphur Springs, Virginia, with another couple. The Coons's favorite destination was Mexico. "Owen and Louise were completely happy when they'd go to Mexico together for a couple of weeks," Eleanor said.

Despite his reverence for college education, none of Owen's three children graduated from college. Eleanor left Ferry Hall after marrying Louis. They saw each other across a room, and fell in love. According to family lore, Owen gave Louis a thorough check and announced to Eleanor: "You've found a good man."

After graduating from Cranbrook, Harry enrolled at Northwestern and majored in speech. But he dropped out to play the drums and vibra-harp with Ben Bernie's Lads, a band named for radio star Bernie, who composed "Sweet Georgia Brown" and popularized the expression "Yowsah, yowsah, yowsah." Harry took his first car, a 1939 Plymouth, down to Texas, but soon found that band life was grueling. He reenrolled at Northwestern, but dropped out to enlist in the Navy at his father's suggestion. Harry was stationed at Great Lakes Naval Training Center, about 20 miles north of Evanston, during the first part of World War II. He joined about 350 other musicians in the Band and Entertainment Department, and the war was something of a dream-come-true for the young drummer. He later served as the band director of the Navy Mine Depot near Yorktown, Virginia, and made money on the side playing dances. By the time the war was over, Harry felt far from academia, and never returned to college.

Owen L. Coon Jr. found school to be particularly difficult during the years his father was alive. He graduated from Evanston Township High School and attended a half-year of college before being called into military service. Owen Jr. served in the Air Force for four years, flying missions over North Korea as a gunner on a B-26 attack bomber. His plane and crew were shot down three times, and he was decorated with several medals. He had two daughters, Elizabeth and Susan, with his first wife, Anne, and later had one son, Owen L. Coon III, known as Trey, with his second wife, Suzanne Blesius. Owen Jr.'s love for fast cars became his passion, as he became a professional racecar driver. He gave up car racing before his second marriage, however, and became a successful business executive in mergers, placements, and acquisitions.

The senior Owen worried constantly about the well being of his children, especially during the forties as they reached adulthood. Eleanor gave birth to her first daughter, Mary Ellen Scott, on December 23, 1940. Although thrilled with his first granddaughter, Owen worried that Eleanor and Louis, a graduate student in chemistry, were not acting responsibly by having children so soon.

"Louise and I have always thought a great deal of Louis, and although they eloped to be married, that did not cause us any particular concern because they both seemed quite happy and contented together," Owen wrote in the mid-forties. "It is true they did not have proper finances, but we made the shortage up to them by allowing sufficient funds to be released to Eleanor out of one of the trust funds which long ago I established for her.

This enabled them to have enough money but not too much to get along until Louis was in a position to carry the load himself."

By 1943, however, Owen's relationship with Eleanor had once again deteriorated. He felt that she lacked discipline and lacked respect for Louise and him. Eleanor, he wrote, has been "my primary worry and is today my primary problem." He continued to blame his mother, Rose, for the difficulties in his relationship with his daughter. He confronted Rose directly and told her to stay out of Eleanor's affairs. In a series of intimidating letters, he made it clear that he would cut off his relationship with his mother unless she followed his detailed suggestions. "Why you allowed your attachment for Eleanor to blind you to what we were doing is something I have never been able to find out," he wrote. "What business was it of yours, anyhow—may I ask in a nice way? She was your grandchild, yes; but our child—our child to raise as we (Louise and I) thought best. It was our business, our job, not yours." And in a letter dated May 10, 1943, he gave his mother this ultimatum:

> Dear Mother,
> What is the solution of this "mess"? Emotions cannot solve it. It can be only solved by a simple course of action—my suggestions are as follows:
>
> (1)—You should say nothing against Louise and myself to anyone at any time—regardless of whether you think we are right or wrong as to any course we follow with Eleanor. If you do not agree with what we are doing—say nothing. If you cannot say anything good about us—say nothing.
>
> (2)—You should have no contact with any member of the Wright family, directly or indirectly.
>
> (3)—You should have no contact with Eleanor—directly or indirectly, by letter, by phone, or in person, for the present, and until she changes her entire attitude toward Louise and myself and my home. She is no part of the Coon family, and I want nothing more to do with her. Whether she changes it or not is up

to her. In the meantime, it is up to you to show loyalty to me first—showing confidence in my judgment and sincerity, by following blindly my leadership in this matter. By doing this, I shall know at last your loyalty and love to me comes ahead of loyalty and love to Eleanor. If Eleanor contacts you, you should tell her that until she makes her "peace" with her father, as he thinks best, you should not desire to have her contact you in any manner. In the meantime, you should give her no money.

The above three things are all that need to be done. Nothing will be gained in talking about this matter between us. I have resorted to use of letters in order that calmer thinking about this matter might result. Your attitude on the matter should be that I am right—even if within yourself you think I am wrong. Your troubles have arisen solely from trying to run someone else's business for them.

If you are willing to follow the policy outlined in this letter—may I suggest you invite Louise and me up to see you, or phone us that you would like to go out to dinner on a Sunday with us. We will accept the invitation, if it is given—no word of the past will be mentioned—we will all turn over "a new leaf." However, do not so invite us unless you are willing to follow this policy—because if you do invite us and then follow a different policy than stated above, our relationships as Mother and son will be thereafter ended.

I assure you if you will only accept and follow the policy I have suggested, no son and daughter-in-law will try harder to make your remaining days happier than will Louise and I. We love you Mother, even though you may think otherwise.
Love,
Owen

On November 21, 1943, Eleanor and Louis's second daughter, Virginia Anne Scott, was born with serious birth defects. She suffered from mental retardation, probably due to the fact that Eleanor had the German measles during her pregnancy. "The effect of Virginia was profound," says Eleanor's oldest daughter, who today is Mary Ellen Segall. Life as Virginia's mother challenged Eleanor to her soul, Mary Ellen said.

It was true; Eleanor's life changed dramatically after the birth of Virginia Anne. "I really don't ask for much out of life—my husband and my children to be all right—and a little home of our own, but I guess that is asking for too much," Eleanor wrote to her father in early 1944, after asking him to help make a down payment on a house. "The baby is the same—never changes. How she lives on is a mystery to me."

Eleanor's request came at a time when Owen was determined to hold the line on lavishing money on his daughter. The timing of his toughness could not have been worse—for this was a moment of true crisis for Eleanor. Owen wrote to Eleanor, "It is true, of course, that I could buy the house for you and give it to you—but I have become firmly convinced that this is not the way to go at the job of raising one's children. It is certainly not my intention to allow the money which I have accumulated to be used to spoil my children. I have found that money can frequently do more damage than it can good."

Eleanor responded by writing that she and Louis would start repaying the $2,000 that Owen loaned them over three years while he was in graduate school studying chemistry. "The fact that he stayed in school too long and incurred too much indebtedness is our mistake and one which we will have to rectify by paying it back," she wrote.

In early 1944, Louis got a job working at Abbott Laboratories in North Chicago. He wrote that the job, in penicillin production, was in the best department at Abbott from the standpoint of draft deferment, money, and a chance for advancement. But Eleanor desperately wanted a house because she expected that Louis would soon be drafted into the military. "The fact that I can never have any more children and that V. Anne will never be normal if she lives is of far more importance to me than anything else," she wrote. "The only reason that I wrote that letter to you about a home is that I wanted to feel more secure when Louis goes. Undoubtedly the time will come when he will have to go."

And in March of 1944, she wrote:

> Right now I have everything that I need. Food.
> Clothing and shelter. From your one remark, I was
> disappointed that you did not know me better. I gath-
> er you still think I am either a silly girl or one who
> is not very capable, if I allowed money to go to my
> head. You don't seem to realize that money is a very
> secondary thing to me. It's awful, Dad, to stand by
> day in and day out and see your baby suffering and
> making no development. Why such a thing should
> happen to a little baby who did not ask to be brought
> into this world, I will never know the answer. If
> Louis and I have done things which we should be
> punished for, that is all right; but she has done noth-
> ing. It makes one doubt faith.

Owen offered a surprising philosophical reply. He was a man of
action who worked hard to make his mark in the world. But, as this next
letter reveals, he saw God-made limits to man-made dreams:

> I realize that both of you are disheartened over Vir-
> ginia Anne. So are Mom and I—by more than words
> can express. Such things, however, are matters over
> which we have no control. It does hurt me, how-
> ever, immensely to have you think that because such
> things occur, there is perhaps reason to doubt one's
> faith in God. There is much indeed that the two of
> you have yet to learn. The coming years will bring
> more clear analysis and clearer thinking on such mat-
> ters. A God does not exist to grant our wishes as
> we would like to have them granted to us. There are
> unchanging natural, physical, and moral laws which
> God has established with which to run the universe
> and the people that are in it. Those laws cannot be
> changed to satisfy the whims of everyone on this
> universe. If such were done, nothing but chaos and
> confusion would result. It is up to us as individuals

on this universe to discover what all those laws are
and then so plan our lives that we do not violate any
of such laws or rules. When such is done, we all
become happier individuals, make less mistakes and
have far less heartaches.

Owen ended the letter with a discomforting logic. "What rules
have been violated by you, or ourselves, or our ancestors that have caused
this condition, we do not know," he wrote. "Perhaps we will never know.
All we do know, however, is that somebody, somewhere, somehow down
along the line has made a mistake and has violated one of these laws
and rules. Therefore, let us not doubt our faith or blame a God, but
rather blame ourselves and try to find out what we have done that is
wrong—and try to so plan our lives in the future that such things may
not further occur."

Eleanor, somewhat reluctantly, accepted Owen's decision not to
help on the down payment. "Well enough of my worries," she wrote.
"It does make me happy to see that you have achieved so much—a happy
home, a fine wife and mother, family position, money, and success in
general. You went thru hell to get them. You deserved them."

As it became apparent that Virginia Anne was severely mentally
handicapped, Eleanor again turned to her father for help. She wanted to
give her daughter private care and, of course, Owen could afford to pay
for it. But Owen disagreed with her idea. He said the child could live a
long time, and suggested that his daughter give up custody of Virginia
Anne and make her a ward of the state. Eleanor trusted Owen's judgment, and came to believe he was absolutely right. "I can't tell you the
help my father was to me in going through that," she said sixty years
later. "He would say, 'What's the matter, honey?' He tried to help."

Eleanor's daughter Mary Ellen agrees that the decision to give
up custody was correct. "It would have been an incredible burden to
keep Virginia Anne in our house," she said. "I haven't seen her since she
left home. I recall her in a limousine going from one place to another."

Sean Harris, a researcher studying the history of the state's
mental institutions, said that Owen's decision was in keeping with the
times. From the 1920s through the 1940s, it was common to commit
the severely disabled to institutional care. The idea, he said, was to put
them away and sterilize them.

It is difficult to assess Owen's handling of this matter more than a half century later. What made it a particularly difficult decision, no doubt, was that he had the money to put Virginia Anne in a private-care facility. "It's somewhat surprising to see how quickly she [Eleanor] acted to give up custody," said Linda A. Teplin, a professor of psychiatry at Northwestern University who was asked to give insight into the decision. "These are huge issues that still have an impact on the family."

‡    ‡    ‡    ‡

ELEANOR AND LOUIS SCOTT divorced in 1945. "Louise and I have been very careful to stay out of the affairs of Eleanor and Louis ever since their marriage, except that occasionally I have tried to give Louis helpful advice regarding bettering his employment whenever he asked me for such advice and help," Owen wrote after the divorce. "Our attitude has been that we should not get down into the private affairs of our children, but should stay aloof from them in order not to become entangled in any matters except where we were asked to do so by them."

Owen, in fact, did anything but stay aloof. In 1944 or 1945, before the divorce, Eleanor came crying to her father about her husband. She suspected—as did Owen and Louise—that he was doing more than working late at the office when he was away from home so many nights.

Perhaps with good intentions, Owen hired a private investigator to shadow his son-in-law. "I decided secretly, however, that in order to help her I would check into the situation to find out what Louis was doing, and if I found that her suspicions were not confirmed I would then be able to disabuse her mind so completely that harmony and trust would again prevail in their house," Owen wrote. "Without telling Eleanor anything about it, therefore, Louise and I arranged to have one of our skip tracers, a man by the name of Simpson, follow Louis on the evening when he and a group of his friends at the plant made a practice of bowling on Howard Avenue."

Owen learned that Louis was involved in a love affair with a co-worker, and he told his daughter. "It was up to her what she wanted to do, if anything," he wrote. Eleanor also discovered that Louis had been having other affairs. Confronted with this, Louis did not seek forgiveness, but told Eleanor he would come back to her only if she agreed never again to see Owen and Louise.

Eleanor filed for divorce.

"I am sure you can realize how broken up we have all been over this situation," Owen wrote. "Personally, I had looked forward to the time when, after the war, I would purchase a chemical plant for Louis and place him in charge, and help him in all the ways that a father should help his son or son-in-law."

After the divorce, Eleanor moved to Estes Park, Colorado, with Mary Ellen for several months to reestablish their lives. While there, she started corresponding with her old high school sweetheart, William A. Briggs, who called her and sent ration stamps. Bill Briggs had asked Eleanor to marry him when she was eighteen. He was pleased now to learn she was single again. Eleanor and Mary Ellen moved back to Evanston at Owen's suggestion in the fall of 1945. The following spring, Bill came to visit Eleanor and told her, "Don't leave me." They were married on June 11, 1946, at a Methodist church in New York City. Mary Ellen, though just a child at the time, saw a difference in her mother's face immediately. "Nobody loved her like Bill did. He made us feel secure. He saved us."

‡    ‡    ‡    ‡

HARRY COON WAS MUSIC MAD. He continued to play his Ludwig drums in the basement of the Coons's new home during his first two years at Northwestern. At night, he would sneak off campus to go to the Grand Terrace Casino on the South Side to hear Fletcher Henderson or hang out with Lionel Hampton. "They were very sweet times," he said.

Harry met Alma Louise Seippel when his family moved to Evanston in 1940. She lived across the street. Her father, John Hermann Seippel III, was executive vice president of Montgomery Ward. In 1942, Owen persuaded Harry to enlist in the Navy because Owen was worried that Harry would be drafted and sent overseas to fight on the front line. He continued to see Alma, who had enrolled at Northwestern, while he was stationed at Great Lakes Naval Station. They decided to get married in 1944, but a few days before the scheduled event, Third Class Petty Officer Harry Coon was shipped out to Virginia. "Mr. and Mrs. Owen Lewis Coon," reads a note, "regret that due to their son's military orders they are obliged to recall their invitations for Sunday, the twelfth of March." Harry and Alma still managed to get married just before they left, at an informal ceremony in the First United Methodist Church in Evanston on March 2, 1944. They spent the duration of the war in Virginia, where she attended the College of William and Mary and he was leader of a Navy band. They lived the good life. Alma enjoyed school and Harry earned a better income than the base commander playing music.

Owen liked his new daughter-in-law, and particularly enjoyed her prolific letter writing. "It is more fun hearing from you than going to a movie," he wrote to Alma in an exchange of letters after the marriage. And, somewhat out of character for him, he confided in her. In a June 1944 letter to Alma, Owen assessed his married life:

> I have had to live through some of the hardships and unsettlement of an unsuccessful domestic life, and also have enjoyed all the pleasures in the last fifteen years of a happy, successful home. I crave for you and for Harry all the pleasures and joys of a home such as I have been able to enjoy with Louise in the last fifteen years. You will find that it is not easy to achieve, but once it is achieved, you will find that it means more to you than anything else in the world, and that you would part with anything else but that. ...It takes some work at the job—some giving in on both sides, some planning and thinking, but gee, it's great—the feeling that one gets when success finally comes to one's efforts.

After the war, Owen invited Harry to join him at General Finance and promised to train him. But, Owen warned, it would take years to teach his son all that he knew. "It's not easy to explain to an amateur, but I shall make a start," Owen wrote Harry in 1945. "You will be learning more about the picture for some years to come. It has taken me twenty-five years to create. No one single person knows all about all of its ramifications—not even Byron. Some people know a lot about certain parts of the picture. So you must not get discouraged if you do not see through it all at once—and what makes the wheels go around—and the checks come in."

Following his Navy discharge, Harry enrolled at the Gregg Shorthand College. After a few months, Owen told Harry to sit down and take dictation. "He dictated fast, not a hem or a haw," Harry recalled. "'Now,' Owen said, 'read it back.' When I did, he said: 'Stop the school; you are going to work with me tomorrow.'"

Owen knew the challenge of showing Harry all the intricacies of the loan business. Making money seemed to come easy to Owen, but his letter to Harry showed that was far from the truth.

> It will take time to teach it all to you and then to train your judgment so you will learn that most important thing of all—When to say yes and when to say no, because in reality saying yes and no in my position and in your later life is what makes the checks keep coming instead of being stopped. It is for that reason I want you to be an expert typist and shorthand operator. Then I can gradually train your mind and translate my own thinking and planning and knowledge that has accumulated in the last twenty-five years into yours. I have done it with Byron and Ray and I can do it with you if you are interested and if you will work very hard and if you will learn to take shorthand and type, etc. Byron had only 1½ years of college and has done it. So you can do it as well, but you have to want to and develop will power to overcome all obstacles. There is no such word as can't. You will miss not having had six years in college as it will be that much harder, just as it was for Byron.

> One never stops going to school under my method. One is always learning. One can start any day. The more one studies the more the thinking processes of the mind are developed. The clearer one can think—the more accurate becomes judgment.

To start, Owen suggested that Harry buy *Time* magazine. "Read it from cover to cover," he wrote. "If you do so for five years you will be surprised at the education you have received. Note, I said cover to cover—not just the parts that seem interesting. It will be quite hard at first. When you can do that and it has become a habit let me know and I will give you the next step. Alma might do it also. She knows more about studying than you do, but neither of you yet know much about real mental concentration—on a sustained basis—that is good for twelve hours in a day. Such Harry is what you must acquire in due course. I should attempt to help you acquire it if you want to."

Owen then sent Harry to the branch offices in Boston, Fort Worth, Dallas, and Dayton, Ohio. Harry's job was to write the operations manual for General Finance—detailing how to discount deals and how to make rate charts. "It taught me of his discipline and his knowledge of the business," Harry said. "We talked about the subtle details that made the business work."

Many of the letters that Owen sent to Harry at this time explained how Owen made money.

> You see, our type of money is not the kind you can put in a bank and do nothing with and just be safe—and never take a risk—and spend the principal when you need it. It is not the type you can refuse to do anything with and be safe. In fact all investments are of this type. Things change constantly. What is safe today and should be done becomes unsafe in due course. One's business position must be constantly changed. When you play football you do not take one position and stand there and never move. No—you change constantly your position—and in business you do likewise—for business is a game, fast moving, very thrilling—some losing—some winning every day. Your job is to learn the game so you will know how to make the moves when called for to protect the businesses in which you have an interest, and thereby protect your wife and family financially—otherwise they will not eat three square meals a day.

Some day, Owen wrote, he would give Harry all the details about the things he owns. "You see," Owen wrote, "I could save a great deal of income tax legally and save you folks a lot of inheritance tax when I die by seeing to it while you and Eleanor and Owen were growing up that you were engaging in business, which under my guidance and direction and buying and selling this and that but mostly buying interests in some poor paying business and then me working to make them profitable. Perhaps some day you can do the working instead of me."

Owen repeatedly expressed his worries in the forties about his children's futures. He was determined that Harry, Eleanor, and Owen Jr. meet specific responsibilities before he entrusted them with the family's wealth. He was resolute about not giving them more money than they could handle. "You see Harry," Owen wrote, "I can accumulate wealth—and give it to my children, but after I am gone they will lose it and it will have been a handicap to them if they don't learn in my lifetime from me what makes the wheels go around, what creates wealth and money and the checks that go into one's personal bank account out of which one buys clothes, food, cars, homes, vacations, pays doctor bills, etc."

Owen wrote to Eleanor in 1944 that he had established a trust fund years ago for her, Harry, and Owen Jr. at the Northern Trust and Savings Bank. He had deposited 10,000 shares of General Finance stock into the trust, some of which had since been sold and invested in other securities. "Harry is to be married next month and Mom and I, after talking it over, have come to the conclusion that the trust established for you and also the one for Harry should be turned over to each of you—to use as each of you sees fit," Owen wrote. "I want to do this in order that I can see whether you can take some money without it going to your head—without it spoiling you and without it ruining your ambition."

Soon after Harry's marriage, Owen wrote him a letter that specified his feelings about family wealth. "The children of a man such as myself must learn how to assume responsibility or it is unfair to society not to divert funds to charities that otherwise would be given to the children," Owen wrote Harry. "It is entirely a matter of how you grow up to assume responsibilities, how you learn to administer certain things that I turn your way, that must in the final analysis decide how much I can safely turn over to you. I must not dissipate the results of my lifetime of work. What you get in the end must be determined by what you can handle, what responsibilities you can assume, how you can grow into the job. I assure you I shall help you in every way possible but even a father can help his son only so far—the rest must be done by the son himself."

‡    ‡    ‡    ‡

WORLD WAR II CREATED rapid and monumental change for General Finance. In an attempt to conserve metal for the military, the War Production Board prohibited the production of new cars starting in January 1942, and that, of course, put an end to new car loans. Owen responded quickly. In an attempt to save his finance business, he started purchasing existing car and commercial loans from other finance companies and then started buying other loan companies. With the economy so uncertain, Owen found bargains. In March 1942, he announced the purchase of household loans from Automobile Bonding Company, and its subsidiary, Inland Investment Plan. That same year, General Finance bought automobile loans from four Chicago finance companies for $1 million in cash.

When Owen acquired the Guardian Fidelity Corporation, of Cleveland and Youngstown, Ohio, he announced: "With these additions, wholly owned subsidiaries operate eleven branches in Illinois, Michigan, and Ohio." So instead of contracting in size, Owen expanded General Finance. To keep stoking the engine of General Finance, he needed to raise huge amounts of money. He devised a way to raise funds by what became known as the Harris Plan, or sales-credit plan. Working with banker Vincent Yager, Owen sold car loans to Chicago's Harris Trust and Savings Bank, which agreed to buy installment notes without recourse. General Finance continued to service the loans.

"Under this plan, General Finance was able to do a much larger volume of business without making a permanent increase in its capital because the bank agreed to take the paper, reimbursing the company for its cash outlay," *Finance* magazine wrote. "The finance charges—the difference between the cash paid the borrower [seller of the paper] and the face amount of the notes—were credited to a reserve to take care of past due notes, losses, interest charges, and rebates given on prepayment of notes. From time to time, the bank paid back excess reserves, when these ran more than 8 or 10 percent. The plan gained national recognition and was widely known as the Harris Trust plan."

But by 1943, and for the duration of the war, General Finance was mostly out of the car finance business. Its retail automobile financing dropped from $55 million in 1940 to $26 million in 1941, to $6 million in 1942 and to $1 million in 1943. Wholesale financing of automobile dealer stock dropped from $29 million in 1941 to $7 million in 1942 and $5 million in 1943. And the company's consumer loan business dropped from $1.9 million in 1941 to $1.1 million in 1942 and $320,000 in 1943.

To keep its loan business alive, General Finance started making large loans to industrial companies with war contracts. General Finance's new industrial loan business started in 1942. In 1943, the company lent $46 million to industries. In 1944, it lent more than $100 million. "Loans were made against accounts receivable, inventories, warehouse stocks, machinery and equipment, and on other collateral which was normally not acceptable to banks," wrote *Fortune* magazine. "During 1944, the volume of business done in accounts receivable and in other forms of commercial borrowing topped $102 million." The company's income fluctuated wildly during the turbulent early years of the 1940s, according to its annual reports. General Finance reported $43 million in consolidated business volume in 1940, $57 million in 1941, $34 million in 1942, $65 million in 1943, $128 million in 1944 and $122 million in 1945.

Once he started his industrial loan business, Owen began thinking about purchasing industrial companies outright. On March 10, 1942, the General Finance charter was amended at its annual meeting of stockholders, giving the company the ability to manufacture, buy and sell commodities. This was a bold and aggressive move. Instead of being driven under by the war restrictions, Owen took advantage of them—helping the nation as well. General Finance's 1943 annual report stated the firm's three major objectives were:

> 1. To have the company make a substantial contribution to the war effort.

> 2. To keep capital and credit lines safely and productively at work.

> 3. To maintain dividend payments on both the preferred and common shares.

General Finance bought controlling interest of six manufacturing companies during the war and made them divisions of the company. "It did not take Owen Coon long to shift into industrial financing to make loans to companies holding war contracts and to acquire companies as subsidiaries, which manufactured supplies for the war effort and had good postwar prospects," *Finance* wrote. "It is doubtful if any finance company devoted its capital to such an all-out war effort as did General Finance Corporation, under the direction of this fast moving, straight thinking executive."

Here is what General Finance purchased:

—Hanlon-Waters of Tulsa, Oklahoma, a company that built pipes and pumps to move gasoline and drinkable water to all major European and Asian battlefronts. During the height of the war, soldiers laid as much as seventy miles of Hanlon pipeline a day, feeding gasoline to Lieutenant General George S. Patton's armored forces in 1944 to help him drive forward on the battlefields.

—Climax Engineering Company, of Clinton, Iowa, which built electric generators to light airfields, diesel engines, and heavy-duty gas and gasoline engines. During the forties, Climax began building oil field drilling and pumping engines, generating sets, and industrial power units.

—McAlear Manufacturing Company, of Chicago, which built precision control instruments, regulators and valves used in petroleum fields, chemical and power plants as well as Navy landing barges, fighting ships, and aircraft carriers.

"Without precision control instruments, many war-vital industrial processes would be impossible," the General Finance annual report stated. "There could be no high octane (aviation) gasoline—no synthetic rubber. Our planes would be slower than Axis planes."

—Bi-Metallic Products Corporation, which built iron hand tools with non-critical metal by using a special hardening process.

—Simmons Manufacturing Company, an Ashland, Ohio, company that built hydraulic equipment that operated aircraft landing gear, wing flaps, and bomb bay doors.

—Morrow Manufacturing Company, of Wellston, Ohio, which built barges and cranes as well as equipment for coal mines, conveyors, coal washers, dumps, bins, car hauls, and elevators.

Owen was proud of his company's role in the war effort. "Nearly $50 million of your company's funds, in the past year, has been employed for financing bomb parts, tank parts, boats, engines, motors, tents, parachute hardware, generating sets, milling machines, prefabricated defense housing, barracks, Army cots, cargo bags, fluorspar, dried egg powder, rations, and other war material," the 1943 annual report announced. The following year, the annual report boasted, "From the day of Pearl Harbor, your company has supplied liberal financing to industry for the production of munitions, equipment, food products, and other essentials of modern warfare. General Finance will continue to do so as long in the future as required."

Owen was not only transforming the company to respond to the war, but was also looking toward the post-war years. He wrote in 1943 that the company was not forsaking the car industry. "Contacts are being maintained with dealers, and as quickly as new car production is resumed your company expects to regain its former larger volume in this field," he wrote.

Owen said he expected that General Finance also would play a role in the expanding market of consumer financing after the war and would continue its new role financing industries and manufacturing products. The 1944 annual report presented General Finance Corporation as a conglomerate. The opening pages profiled a boundless company that now included offices in Chicago; Detroit; St. Louis; Philadelphia; Milwaukee; Portland, Oregon, and Decatur, Illinois, as well as factories in Chicago; Clinton, Iowa; Tulsa, Oklahoma; and Wellston and Ashland, Ohio. By 1944, General Finance Corporation now included the General Finance Loan Company, the GFC Credit Company, GFC Insurance Exchange Agency, Mid-States Insurance Company, Climax Engineering Company, Hanlon-Waters, McAlear Manufacturing Company, Bi-Metallic Products Corporation and a new division called General International.

The year 1944 was a time of celebration for Owen and his company. The annual report included financial figures from the first twenty years of Motor Assurance Company and General Finance Corporation. "The progress this comparison shows requires little amplification," Owen wrote. "Suffice to say that the company's average volume of business today is greater than total resources twenty years ago." As the war progressed and the War Production Board eased restrictions, many manufacturers turned to General Finance for cash to buy material, machinery, and plants to make goods for civilian consumers.

Owen saw a bright future. The plants he owned had become highly efficient industries. Climax Industries, for example, was operating with three shifts a day for six days a week, turning out vital war material. Owen fully expected that these factories would be retooled to produce wholesale goods after the war. "When the time comes to turn the machinery of war to the production of civilian goods, no General Finance customer will have to wait for his assets to become liquid before he can set in motion the wheels of consumer production," he wrote.

The company also diversified into real estate. In 1943, General Finance bought control of the Wacker Corporation, which owned title to the Civic Opera House at 20 Wacker Drive in downtown Chicago. Owen picked up the forty-five-story limestone skyscraper, built for $23 million by utilities magnate Samuel Insull in 1931, on what Owen called a "toothpick equity." He gave the Chicago Opera Company $125,000 in cash to pay off its debts, and assumed a $9.9 million first mortgage. "The transaction, under which title to the opera building passes to the finance company, is one of the largest real estate operations in Chicago in recent years," wrote a Chicago newspaper. The building was the city's second largest and was fully rented.

Owen's moves were getting noticed. Soon after the purchase of the opera house, the *Chicago Tribune* outlined General Finance's transformation in an article entitled "Speed General Finance Shift Into Industry." In the April 3, 1943, article, Owen said he planned to change the name of General Finance to General Industries, or a similar name, to reflect the changes of the company.

"Our name will be changed before the end of the year," Owen told a reporter by phone from the Climax headquarters in Clinton. "We would have changed the name before this, but have been too busy to carry out the formalities. We rapidly are becoming what might be termed an industrial holding company, and probably will end up with a group of businesses owned outright. We will, of course, not neglect the sales financing business when the war is over."

‡   ‡   ‡   ‡

DIRECTING GENERAL FINANCE CORPORATION was but one part of Owen's war effort. In 1943, he was selected chairman of the suburban division of the Community and War Fund of Metropolitan Chicago. The following year, he was named chairman of the city division. The fund raised money for the war through civilian donations.

Owen also was appointed by the Illinois State War Chest and National War Fund to raise money for the United Service Organizations and fifteen war relief agencies in Cook, DuPage, and Lake counties. The goal was to raise money from 90,000 small businesses in Chicago and its suburbs.

After Owen was elected chairman of the suburban division, the *Evanston Review* wrote: "Mr. Coon, in accepting the appointment, started to work immediately to set up his division, which entails dividing his territory into six districts and appointing a vice chairman for each district." At the same time, Owen was active in his local Evanston war drive, first as a contributor and then as a leader.

A 1944 photo in the *Evanston Review* shows Owen and other Evanston businessmen posing in the office of Augustus Knight, chairman of the Evanston War Finance committee. They were purchasing $1 million in war bonds. Owen bought $335,000 worth of bonds to help boost the Evanston Bond Campaign to $4.6 million. The article quoted Knight as saying that he was worried that Evanston would not meet its $6.5 million quota despite the city's fine reputation in raising war bonds and stamps.

To help meet the quota, Owen was elected president of the Evanston War Chest in March 1944. "When Owen L. Coon, general chairman, announced the figures for the divisions and for the ten-ward district there was a suspense until the total for the entire campaign was announced," a local paper reported. "The 101 percent sounded 'mighty good' to the leaders who for four weeks had been bending every effort possible to raise the quota in the concentrated period."

All three of Owen's children recall him standing at the speaker's podium at fundraising events during World War II. This was when they saw their father at his best, adroitly making use of all he had learned from Clarion Hardy. "He was big on war drives," Owen Coon Jr. recalled. "Mom and I would travel to Park Ridge and places like that to watch him give speeches. Everybody knew him or knew of him. I remember listening to a lot of speeches." Recalled Harry: "He was a great public speaker who could mesmerize the crowd." And Eleanor: "He was a fabulous speaker who could control the audience. He had such driving ambition to do good."

‡ ‡ ‡ ‡

NORTHWESTERN UNIVERSITY, TOO, was changed dramatically by the war. The university became something of a military center—providing facilities for the War Department, Army, Navy and Civil Aeronautics Administration. The university provided offices for the administration of Selective Service and space for a new Reserve Midshipmen's Training Unit and Naval Aviation Preparatory Program, among many others. During the war, more than 400 faculty members were granted leaves of absence to serve in the armed forces or other government war-related activities.

Despite the increased challenge of running General Finance during the war, Owen turned more of his attention toward the university. He was determined that his Hardy Scholarships would continue after his death. In 1943, he asked his attorney to work on a contract specifying his will as a permanent endowment fund for the Hardy Scholarships. "I do not think it advisable for anyone to commit himself for a sum as large as $150,000," his attorney, Richard Oldberg, wrote to Owen. "There have been many instances of contracts to bequeath fixed sums which have worked out so as to leave little or nothing to the decedent's family. I realize you have set up trusts for your family but the fact of the matter is that the trusts themselves will probably not be any too well off if, at your death, it is difficult for your executors to pay over the $150,000. This is because most of your eggs are in the same basket so that the trust will probably suffer if your personal estate suffers. I think you ought to make the amount a great deal smaller or, preferably, make it in terms of a fixed percentage of your net estate after taxes with a maximum dollar amount."

Owen reluctantly agreed. A few days after his birthday, however, Owen wrote to Northwestern's Thomas Gonser that he wanted to set up a new scholarship. "Enclosed you will find a check for $1,000, which was given to me on July 1st, 1944, as a birthday present by my mother on the occasion of my fiftieth birthday," he wrote. "After some conversation with her and my brother as to what should be done with this money, I have decided to make it the first installment on the establishment in due course of two, and probably four, scholarships to be permanently endowed in due course."

The scholarships, named the James S. Coon Scholarships in honor of Owen's father who died in 1939, were to be used by "some deserving boy" who graduates from Rantoul High School and attends Northwestern University. The school later broadened the scholarship to include any "deserving student." Owen wrote: "As you know, three men have left a considerable impression upon my life—my father, Clarion DeWitt Hardy, and Arthur Newton. I have wanted to do something to preserve the memory of each of them—in a form that did not show itself in buildings or stone and mortar, but rather in the lives of some boys who needed financial help to round out their education." Owen wrote that he would work out plans and details on the new fund, which he believed his mother and brother would want to supplement.

That same year, Owen set up the Arthur W. Newton Fellowship to train students in management, finance and credit. The fund, named in honor of the retired vice president of First National Bank of Chicago who had advised and lent money to Owen during the thirties, was for Northwestern University graduate students in the School of Commerce to study consumer finance. Newton, who joined the bank in 1906, is often called the grandfather of the automobile finance business because he lent money to the car-loan industry despite severe criticism from fellow bankers. The credit he extended was called "Newton's tin can loans."

‡   ‡   ‡   ‡

AMONG HIS MANY INTERESTS, Owen Coon was devoted to the First Methodist Church of Evanston. He loved attending church on Sundays, although he always arrived late and had to sit up in the balcony, his children recall. As head of the First Methodist Church finance committee for several years, he wrote to church members every year asking for donations. His pleas give insight into his views as a benefactor. One year he wrote:

> As a boy of 12, I had my first experience in seeing a church balance its budget. My father took me to a meeting of the official board of our church in a small town in central Illinois. The meeting opened with a prayer by the minister. The chairman stated the amount of the budget, a larger amount than any previous one because of increased current expenses and the deficit remaining from the building of a new church home. Then the chairman announced his personal pledge. One by one, around the table, each member arose and made his pledge.
>
> To reach the goal, a second 'round' of pledges—and a third—were necessary. Finally, the meeting closed

106

with the singing of 'Praise God From Whom All Blessings Flow.'

The budget had been raised in less than an hour. "Those men knew that they wanted their church and that they must contribute towards its support," he wrote. "They gave voluntarily without urgent solicitation according to their own financial ability. No one criticized the amount anyone gave. No one told anyone what he should give."

In his solicitation letter for another year, he wrote: "Let us all experience the joy that comes when one silently and alone decides the amount of his obligation to a worthy cause—and subscribes to it voluntarily without urgent personal solicitation—and goes on his way with the inner satisfaction of a deed well done, of a moral obligation accepted and satisfied, of having put back into the world something of service to others in return for what has been received."

This was Owen Coon's philosophy.

‡    ‡    ‡    ‡

In 1935, General Finance Corporation had five branch offices and fifty-five employees. Ten difficult years later—years of Depression and war—the company had forty branch offices and 286 employees. *Finance* magazine, in a September 10, 1945, article entitled "Owen Coon Finds the Way," wrote that Owen had built up the net worth of General Finance Corporation from $100,000 to $7.2 million by the end of the war. "Reviewing all of these accomplishments, it does not seem possible that a single individual could jam pack so many achievements within the span of the war years," the magazine reported. "The vast increase in net worth has been achieved by a simple but distinctive system of capital building—through the retention of earnings and the use of preferred stock to pay for the acquisition of assets and other companies. In only one instance—the first sale of $750,000 in subordinated debentures—was capital raised at the expense of diluting common stock holding to any material extent."

For the record, General Finance's net income rose during most of the war years: $460,000 in 1941, $630,244 in 1942, $989,786 in 1943, and $653,991 in 1944. The company's net income for the first six months of 1945 was already at $841,645 when the war came to an end. And for the record, Owen was greatly helped by his team of executives.

Byron Coon served as president. Lyle Titus was secretary. Ray Titus was in charge of collection activities, such as the repossession of used cars. Karl Oldberg, older brother of attorney Richard Oldberg, was in charge of the wholesale division. Chester "Bud" Cofoid and later Ed McGrath ran the automobile discount division. E. F. "Al" Wonderlic was in charge of the small loan division. And Walter P. Maher, credit manager, reviewed every deal personally. "He was one of the smartest guys in the company," Harry Coon said, "because you had to know what you are doing with conditional sales contracts, whether or not you should repurchase, whether you had non-recourse, how much hedging you would do with these guys. Dealers would shaft it to you unless you were shrewd."

The top executives were guided by Owen's simple business plan. "The method I have used is to buy something cheap—make it valuable, keep it, and let it grow," he wrote.

And, as he wrote to Harry and Alma, he avoided paying heavy taxes by limiting the amount of dividends paid out:

> We have low dividends in all our companies—enough to provide a comfortable, even luxurious living and keep the earnings in the companies themselves and let the companies grow and expand and buy other businesses and companies. ...It is a simple plan—so simple that many people, in fact few people, have sense enough to see it and do it. Learn this lesson and follow it in the future years. It will mean much to you, but under such a plan the debts of such companies must always be kept within bounds. Defaulted debts and low earnings can destroy the whole structure. Under such a plan the company itself becomes a safety deposit box holding the cash we would otherwise have in our own bank accounts.

The book value of the family increased about $250,000 a year, Owen estimated. But he warned that there are no guarantees. "Learn to always be modest notwithstanding having wealth," he advised Alma and Harry. "Never let it spoil you. Be democratic. Never be stuck up or better than other people. Always work hard. It's the only way you can keep money and wealth from ruining you and destroying happiness. Don't be a playgirl or playboy, and have a serious purpose in life."

# CHAPTER SIX

# Post-War Economics

As World War II wound down to a victorious conclusion, Owen Coon was among the first to purchase a Cadillac limousine. He hired a Northwestern University student as a chauffeur so that he could work on a Dictaphone as he rode downtown to General Finance's new corporate headquarters in Chicago's 184 West Lake Building. "He would step out of the car, go to his desk and continue working," Owen Jr. recalled.

Owen Sr. correctly predicted that the production of cars would not start up again until Germany and Japan surrendered. And he correctly foretold that demand would boom after the war. He estimated that a minimum of 6 million cars, more than the all-time peak of 5.2 million cars in 1929, would be built each year following a return to peace. He was right.

In 1945, Owen was determined to retool his factories to make consumer products. The company set up a new division to acquire and develop products, and an industrial engineering division to plan production. Meanwhile, he established General International as a new division to position the company for world trading, the apparent next frontier after the war. "The eyes of industry are fast focusing on foreign markets," he observed.

Several of General Finance's manufacturing interests were readied for peacetime production. Owen folded Hanlon-Waters into McAlear Manufacturing Company and sold Bi-Metallic Products Corporation. Simmons Manufacturing Company started making bumper jacks for cars and auto parts. Climax Engineering started manufacturing farm products—from electric field lights to the Till-Master, a revolutionary tractor that could plow, disc and harrow a farm field in one swoop. At first, Owen expected to remain in manufacturing. According to Charles Wonderlich Jr., whose father would later become president of General Finance, Owen bought iron from the Normandy beachheads, wanting to use it for scrap.

Likewise, Owen expected to continue making loans to large industries. "Though inaugurated by the company during the war years, and developed to a peak volume of $92 million a year, industrial financing should not be regarded as a wartime expedient only," he wrote in the 1945 annual report. "The need for this financial service continues almost as great in time of peace. It is essential to business enterprises whose growth opportunities are greater than their financial resources. Additional management and sales personnel, added to both divisions, has helped your company to get its postwar plans underway quickly and efficiently."

Owen also began to expand the finance division—consisting of auto finance and small consumer loans. By the end of 1945, General Finance had consumer offices in major cities throughout the East, Midwest, and South. "It was necessary to establish these offices considerably in advance of the resumption of automobile manufacturing and to staff them with capable, experienced people," he wrote. "Such expenses for rents and salaries have been sizable, but essential for competitive reasons."

In August 1945, the month America celebrated Victory over Japan Day, Owen purchased the twenty-eight-story building at 184 West Lake Street to serve as General Finance's new home. He bought the building, at the northeast corner of Lake and Wells streets, for $1.65 million, making a ten percent down payment through a private corporation he set up with family members and business partners. During the war, this building—with lush, deep, red African marble on the first floor and brass fixtures throughout—was one of Chicago's most profitable pieces of real estate. Tenants included the Blue Network (ABC), the Red Network (NBC), the Army, and other governmental agencies. Owen believed that rents could be raised to return an even greater profit.

General Finance occupied the second through fifth floors and parts of the seventh floor. Its subsidiaries, such as Climax Industries, occupied other offices in the building. When Owen purchased the skyscraper, he figured that his private corporation would soon sell the building to General Finance, turning a small profit. The building, he thought, would be an excellent investment for the firm. But in February 1946, he changed his mind. He wrote his fellow directors at General Finance that they should turn down his offer to purchase equity in the Lake Street building. It was a decision in keeping with a new direction Owen had decided General Finance should take. He wanted the company to return to automobile financing, and he recommended that it sell all of its manufacturing and real estate interests.

Owen had kept General Finance afloat during the war by shrewdly acquiring and operating factories related to the war effort. But once the war was over, he realized that the time for diversification was over. He wrote to the board that he had recently promised outside investors and bankers that General Finance would return to its base business.

> The prospectus you all signed also touches on this. The credit reputation of this company has been built on the fact that I have consistently made "my word as good as a secured bond" and as long as I am chairman of the board of this company I expect to continue such a policy.

> It is only by doing so that the credit reputation of this company can be consistently maintained on a plan that enables us to borrow money in the open market at 3/4 of 1 percent, a rate as low or lower than that paid by the public for the purchase of certificates of indebtedness of the U.S. Government. Whenever the head of this company does not make his word as good as a secured bond, then we might as well fold up, liquidate, and quit business.

Owen was seldom boastful, but in this letter he was adamant that he personally was behind the success of General Finance—as a businessman and as a person. Now, he wrote, it was time to follow his lead and return to automobile financing:

> This business of ours is based upon faith, on credit, and on the oral representations of its officers, and once they are given they must be lived up to faithfully without equivocation—by cutting all

corners square and not rounding them! In 1934,
when I first became president of the company,
what little credit you had was at a 10 percent
simple interest rate from another finance company.
The decline in our interest rate since that date has
not happened by accident, nor is it entirely the
result of economic conditions. Some sizable portion of the cause lies in my steadfast pursuit of the
policy stated in this paragraph.

Owen made no bones about it: He was the company and was
responsible for the company's success.

I have always followed a policy that whenever I
could not solve a corporate problem by the use
of corporate funds, I would step into the breach
personally with any funds or security or credit that
I had, to accomplish a proper corporate purpose.
All of the bankers in this country with whom we
do business know that if anything should happen
to General Finance, the writer would pledge every
dime of his net worth quickly, willingly, and without hesitation to protect every creditor from loss to
the best of my ability, and work until I died to pay
off without loss. It is only as I follow such a policy
and make the deed correspond to the word that this
company will continue to thrive and succeed and
have an unlimited supply of bank credit. I do not
expect to change this policy. It is simply impossible
for me to do so.

The end of the war, he wrote, demanded a corporate rethinking.
But he warned that General Finance should be leery about embarking in
new directions. He wrote:

I have not assumed that we would develop into a
real estate holding company, nor an industrial holding company, nor an investment trust. ...If such

is to be your policy you need a different set of officers with different backgrounds and experience than what you have now. The time has long since arrived to start making more and more of our capital flow back into the finance business (or else get out of it entirely).

Owen argued that General Finance must return to its original mission. Diversification was an absolute necessity during the war, he said, but now it was time to sell off the factories. He was working hard to negotiate the sale of all manufacturing divisions, he said. "We have diversified far enough," Owen wrote. "I am having too many things to look after as it is—and we must stop diversifying somewhere. As far as I am concerned, that diversification stopped yesterday—not tomorrow. Such has been my policy for some time and is the one which I deem best for the interest of the stockholders."

The board of directors agreed. Owen ended up selling the Lake Street building to outside investors for $2.5 million in 1947, and divested most of the manufacturing companies that General Finance had acquired. He also sold $1.1 million of General Finance's war-related and new consumer credit businesses to Standard Factors, a New York financing company. "It leaves General Finance with three major divisions," wrote General Finance treasurer Robert Scott, "automobile financing, small loans, and insurance related to those two activities. Those are the divisions we had before the war."

‡　　‡　　‡　　‡

LIKE MANY EXECUTIVES in the auto finance industry, Owen always worried that bankers would wake up one day and start loaning money themselves for cars and consumer items. So Owen, as an individual, started investing in banks—as a hedge against the possibility of banks wiping out the entire auto finance industry. In 1939, he bought the small Chicago Terminal National Bank, a neighborhood bank west of the Chicago River. He also served on the board of directors of the Chicago National Bank, on West Monroe Street in Chicago's Loop.

Terminal Bank grew rapidly. Deposits increased from $6 million in 1939 to $32 million in 1945 and earnings increased. In 1946, the bank moved downtown to the corner of LaSalle and Monroe streets. Wrote *Business Week*: "LaSalle Street's seven established banks feel a newcomer's elbow at their ribs. The new neighbor is small, but the big-time Chicago bankers do not laugh it off as a competitor. Rather, they wonder whether it will cut itself a share of their business, develop substantial deposits, and perhaps climb into the big time." Owen was the reason why the established bankers were worried. "What makes it a competitor to take seriously is fiftyish, balding, chunky Owen L. Coon. His sole title in the bank is director, but he owns control and sets the policies."

During the mid-forties, after he had added banks to his family holdings, Owen described the process he used to make money. "Yes, our family type of money is peculiar wealth," he wrote Harry. "This is very valuable but a peculiar kind. It's made up of little pieces of paper representing shares of percentages of ownership in various businesses—a bank, a finance company, etc. Most of the pieces of paper I paid very little for. I bought them when they were not going very good or did not even exist."

Some of the companies, such as the Terminal National Bank, he bought for as low as 2 percent of their asking price because they were nearly worthless. "Not even good for toilet paper," he wrote. "I built up their earning power. ...I attracted business to them, selected good people to run them, saw to it that they were run efficiently and became successful. When such is done such businesses become valuable—wealthy. But, such businesses can become worthless as fast as they become valuable if the wrong people run them, and if people own control of them who do not know how to handle them."

Owen often used the term "wheels" when describing the force behind his business ventures. He wrote Harry:

> So you will see a little now as I will explain in detail later, but it will not do you a damn bit of good ten years after I am dead unless you can develop to know all the wheels of the machine—what makes them go—what the hazards are—when to make them go and when to slow—when to expand and when to contract, etc. You will also learn to look out the windows and think with your mind miles

away—utterly unconscious of what is being said and done around you. You have to do it—to make our family type of money safe—so we can continue to have for our wives and children the things we want them to have. You will also find that with this type of money that one has to keep constantly growing and expanding with ups and downs with stops for breathing, because unless you do you go backward. No business ever stands still. It either goes ahead or goes back. If you don't want it to go back you have to push it ahead.

‡    ‡    ‡    ‡

IN 1945, the Hardy Scholars gathered once again for lunch at the Coons's house. Past and present scholars joined Owen and Louise on May 23 as the war was winding down and the world started to turn to peace. That was the year in which Owen wrote to Clarence Simon, acting dean of Northwestern's School of Speech, that he wanted the Hardy scholarships program to favor male students. Men, he wrote, were more likely to start long careers after graduation and put the ideas of the program into practice. "I am anxious to get this program on a male scholarship basis entirely, or at least up to 80 percent on a male basis," he wrote. Until then, the schol-arships had been given to undergraduate students in commerce, language arts, and speech. A large percentage of speech students were males because many pre-law students saw speech as a way to prepare for law school. In turn, most Hardy applicants were male.

"We have acted on the principle that for the duration and while the number of men is definitely limited we would select the best people available regardless of sex," Owen wrote in 1945. "But that as normal times return we can serve the purposes of these scholarships better by confining them almost exclusively, if indeed not entirely, to men."

Simon did not dispute Owen, but found himself pushing for-ward three women for the 1945-46 scholarship program. "I feel very much pleased with this group of Hardy Scholars, though as you will im-mediately recognize, we are recommending three women and two men," Simon wrote Owen. "I expect, however, that this ratio will be substan-tially altered as more men return to college halls."

Seven of the early Hardy Scholars were women, including Gloria Rensch, one of the original scholars. But by late 1946, Owen decided no more scholarships should go to women. They did not serve the "ultimate purpose" of the program, he wrote. By then, Owen had changed his idea of the scholarships. He wanted his money to be given to high school men entering Northwestern with the hope of becoming political leaders. In 1946, Owen wrote to Simon: "Perhaps I am trying to state in a few words a big dream that we have had; namely that we would like to see Hardy Scholars become leaders in the political life of our country, but in a manner that would make them sufficiently independent financially that in many cases they might be the leaders of a minority instead of a majority."

Owen wanted Hardy Scholars to "assume important roles in the political life of the nation" and raise the integrity and ideals of politics to new levels. To find the proper students, he suggested that the scholarships be limited to students in the School of Speech who took forensics training, because these students were most likely to attend law school.

This was quite a change in his philosophy; he now wanted to create a cadre of independent politicians. Owen wrote school officials that he was willing to support Hardy Scholars through law school and would even help them relocate if they wanted to work for the government. And he wrote that he was willing to help them start law offices and donate to their political campaigns. It didn't matter to what political party his scholars belonged, he wrote. Owen's stated goal was to instill strong ethics all around local, state, and federal governments.

"I think he was a bit naïve in saying that," said Harry Coon, "because he was a staunch conservative, and I think he would have ultimately been bothered if liberals got this scholarship."

"Is the dream too big?" Owen asked. A law professor at Harvard University molded most of the young lawyers who made the New Deal under Roosevelt, Owen wrote. "I have no desire to create any particular kind of New Deal, but only to foster those movements which independent, freethinking students, who later might become interested in the political life of our country, might think fitting and proper."

Northwestern's Simon disagreed with Owen's plan. "Just as good and intelligent prospects prefer to register in the College of Liberal Arts," he wrote Owen. And Simon argued that you don't have to be a lawyer to excel in politics. "Vocational objectives are not sufficiently clarified or settled during high school days," Simon wrote. "In fact the very type of student we prize most highly, who is thoughtful and balanced in his judgment, is apt to be the one to delay his final vocational decision until later in his educational life."

Simon was surprisingly brash with the Northwestern benefactor. "The committee feels very strongly that confining its selection to those who at the close of their high school days have decided on the law as a vocation would not only limit our selection but would give us on the whole a less desirable group from which to choose," he wrote Owen. "Far too often a vocational decision made at this time is made without information, unintelligently, and as a result of following the line of least resistance—forms of decision which have no place in the lives of Hardy Scholars."

Owen and Simon corresponded frequently during 1946, and the interchange helped them both define the scholarship program. It also showed how much they both cared about the Hardy Scholars. "I think it would be most helpful if we could exchange letters on possible differences of opinion between your committee and myself," Owen wrote Simon in November 1946. "I am sure there are no differences that cannot be reconciled, and the best way to do so is to argue about them frankly." Later, Owen wrote: "I need a further letter from you, Si, telling me just what you and the committee want and what should be done. I would like to have this in writing so that I can see it and think about it. Right now there is a blank wall before me and I am afraid you will have to take me by the hand and lead me along the pathway of your thoughts."

And still later, Owen wrote: "Let's argue about it in writing, if you don't mind, because while I am traveling about the country I have more time to read and think things over than when I am in the office." Eventually, Owen agreed with most of Simon's suggestions regarding the administration of the Hardy Scholarships. He concurred that the scholarship should continue to be open to majors outside the speech school and he considered expanding the Hardy Scholarships program to Northwestern's law school. In either case, Coon wrote that he still wanted to give priority to students who would major in law because his first goal was to create public-spirited lawyers.

Owen remained insistent that his program be open only to male students. But Simon responded that the Hardy Scholarship committee—made up of the Northwestern president, director of personnel and School of Speech chairman—must be free to make all final decisions.

118

# Owen Coon
## and the
## American Dream

*Images of a Life*

*Plate 1*  James and Rose Coon on their wedding day in 1892.

*Plate 2*  The Coon home in LeRoy, about 1900.

*Plate 3* Owen as a boy in the late 1890s. Owen split his childhood between Rantoul and LeRoy, Illinois.

*Plate 4* The Rantoul Township High School junior class in 1911.
Owen, at bottom center, excelled at the school.

*Plate* 5   Owen (right) with high school friends. By his senior year, Owen was the leader of the graduating class.

*Plate 6* Owen (right) studies in his Northwestern University dormitory room.

# Northwestern University Law School

## Henry Sargent Towle Prize Debate
### Monday, May 15, 1916.

## QUESTION:

WHEREAS, under the present rule relating to admission to the bar in Illinois, there are required a preliminary education equivalent to that represented by a four year high school and three years' study of law under the direction of an attorney or in a law school, RESOLVED, that the requirement for admission should be increased in one or both these respects.

### CONTESTANTS

| AFFIRMATIVE | NEGATIVE |
|---|---|
| (1) Coon, Owen Lewis | Stelle, Omar Porter |
| (3) Bergesen, Albert Rufus | Dwinell, Bruce Edward |
| Mangan, William Joseph | (2) Traxler, Dean Lake |

#### PRESIDING OFFICER:
Dean John H. Wigmore

#### JUDGES:
THOMAS F. HOLGATE, Dean Northwestern University College of Liberal Arts – *gave me first*

ANDREW R. SHERIFF, Esq., Chairman Committee on Legal Education of Chicago Bar Association – *gave me first*

CHARLES H. WATSON, Esq., of the firm of Hyde, Westbrook and Watson *gave me second*

#### AWARDS:
FIRST PRIZE—One hundred dollars
SECOND PRIZE—Fifty dollars

Eight minutes will be allowed each speaker for presentation of main argument and four minutes for rebuttal

*Plate 7* Owen continued debating for Northwestern while at law school.

*Plate 8* Alice Wright Coon and daughter Eleanor in the early twenties.

*Plate 9* Louise Coon, Owen's second wife, in the late thirties.

*Plate 10* Owen's children: Harry (left), Eleanor and Owen Jr. in the thirties.

*Plate 11* The Coon mansion at 1201 Sheridan in Evanston. Known by the family as "The Hotel," the 22-room house was purchased in 1940.

*Plate 12* Plaque at the entrance of the General Finance Corporation's headquarters at 184 West Lake Street in Chicago.

*Plate 13* Owen Coon (center) is joined on a couch by banker Arthur W. Newton (left) and Byron Coon at a 1947 dinner honoring the Newton Fellowship to train students in management, finance, and credit.

# NORTHWESTERN UNIVERSITY

## CLARION DeWITT HARDY

## SCHOLARSHIPS *in* FORENSICS

*Established by* OWEN L. COON

Announcement of the first awards, full tuition
for one year, to be granted to freshmen entering Northwestern University at the beginning
of the academic year 1935-36

*Plate 14* Announcement of the Hardy Scholarships.

The **Hardy Scholarships** of **Northwestern University** were established in nineteen hundred thirty-five by **Owen L. Coon** in honor of the teacher who contributed most to his education:

**Clarium DeWitt Hardy**

**Evanston, Illinois, Nineteen Hundred and Forty-three.**

*Plate 15* Cover of the Book of the Hardy Scholars.

*Plate 16* Owen's portrait by artist William S. Schwartz unveiled in 1961.

"Your first suggestion that the scholarship should be confined to men is entirely acceptable to the committee," he wrote. "I do think, however, the committee should reserve the right, in highly exceptional cases and with strong supporting evidence, to present a woman candidate with assurance that she will be considered as a possibility." But the university excluded women from Hardy Scholarships until the 1970s.

Professor Ernest Wrange, of the School of Speech, replaced Simon on the Hardy committee when Simon took a year leave of absence in 1947. Wrange wrote to Owen that the committee had discussed his suggestions and come to a consensus: "There is hearty endorsement of your desire to select Hardy Scholars on the basis of their expressed interest and their promise for a career in public life. This provides a splendid objective for the program as well as a definite basis for selecting scholars."

But Wrange wondered if law school was the only area of graduate study that Coon should consider in awarding scholarships. He thought economists, political scientists, and others might have profound impact in public service. "It seems to us that there is much to be said for making the scholarships available at the time of the student's graduation from high school," Wrange wrote. "I say this for two reasons. In the first place, there are many exceptional boys who would never reach Northwestern without financial assistance. The second reason for selecting them upon graduation from high school or early in their university careers is the opportunity it offers for giving them a special type of guidance."

This question was resolved in early 1947 when Owen decided to also provide Hardy Scholarships to students in Northwestern's law school. "In this way," he wrote, "we would avoid the difficulty on the part of undergraduates to make up their minds definitely to enter law or any other profession, and the selection would be made at a point where this decision has been made."

Owen suggested Northwestern appoint two separate boards to administer the separate scholarships. The undergraduate committee would continue to be chaired by Simon. Law school professor James Rahl, an original Hardy Scholar, would chair the law school committee. Owen wrote that he wanted the same principles to apply to the law school scholarships, that of "developing individuals who will enter public life and bring integrity in high places." Owen figured he would set a ceiling of eight law students and eight undergraduate students. The Owen L. Coon Foundation, established in 1946, would pay the tuition of these students and the operating costs of the program. Fourteen Hardy Medals were awarded at the June 1947 commencement.

‡     ‡     ‡     ‡

AT THIS TIME in Owen's life, his first wife, Alice Wright Coon, continued in a strange way to serve as his nemesis. Alice, adjudicated insane by the Kankakee County Court in 1934, filed a petition in 1941 to be restored to reason and was found to be sane by the Kankakee Circuit Court. On February 13, 1942, Judge Rudolph F. Desort entered an order in Cook County Superior Court stipulating that Owen pay Alice $350 per month, up from the 1935 agreement that Owen pay $150 per month. In return, Alice agreed to confirm and ratify their 1929 divorce. For years, Alice's family had threatened to sue Owen to void the divorce, and this would end the threat, Owen thought.

But Alice, through a conservator, did sue Owen in 1946, challenging the divorce. On March 21, she was adjudicated incompetent once again. Her conservator filed a lawsuit in the Superior Court against Owen attempting to vacate the 1929 divorce decree. The lawsuit argued that Owen had used his wealth and power to coerce Alice into the divorce. Owen filed a motion to dismiss the suit and won. Judge Ulysses S. Schwartz ruled in 1947: "Serious charges are made and denied with vehemence characteristic of disputes of this character. In the intervening period, the defendant has remarried and has a child by the second marriage. If the plaintiff is successful, the consequences would be to stigmatize the child as illegitimate and disgrace both families."

Owen's victory was overturned by the Illinois Appellate Court, which ruled that Alice had the right to sue to vacate the divorce.

The appellate judges were critical of Owen's conduct—both before the 1929 divorce and since. The court found that "Owen L. Coon, at the time mentioned, was a man of great wealth, which on information and belief was in excess of $20 million, and was a lawyer; [and] the divorce decree was procured by fraud." Moreover, the court found that "Coon swore falsely at the trial and suborned his father who testified falsely in connection with the alleged desertion." In these years, before the era of no-fault divorce, it was not uncommon for people to manipulate facts to satisfy the grounds of divorce in their state. Owen had asked for the divorce in 1929 on the grounds that Alice had deserted him, which the appellate court determined was not true. "Alice Wright Coon was then there insane and did not have sufficient mental capacity to understand what she was doing," the court ruled.

The decision was quite a condemnation against Owen. The judges further found that Alice, against her will and under the influence of narcotics administered by a nurse hired by Owen Coon, was taken to Wichita, Kansas, following the divorce. Alice, by her conservator, charged that Owen was behind the effort to get her restored to reason in 1941. Her attorneys charged that Owen instigated the petition, despite full knowledge that Alice had never regained her sanity. The attorneys charged that Owen wanted her declared sane in order to ratify the 1929 divorce decree.

On paper, Owen came off as a bully who had spent years manipulating Alice for his own purposes—but the situation was far more complex. Despite years of confrontation by Alice's family and friends, Owen continued to look out for Alice's welfare years after the divorce. For example, he wrote to his daughter Eleanor in November 1946 that she must return soon to Chicago to help her mother prepare for the lawsuit against him.

> Eleanor, your case will come up for trial some time between the 15th and 30th of December. As you know, you should be back here to protect your mother's interests sufficiently in advance to make sure that you have properly prepared your case with your attorney. ...Periodic visits back here to your mother are something that you must make, and of course you will want to do so until the millstone which her relatives have placed around her neck is removed and she is a free agent to do as you and she think best.

Looking back at these many years, Alice's only daughter Eleanor does not believe her father purposefully tried to take advantage of her mother. And despite her love for Alice's family, she remains upset to this day that many of Alice's relatives fought so hard for a piece of Owen's fortune and kept the charges alive for so many years.

‡   ‡   ‡   ‡

By 1946, Owen Coon had begun to think about philanthropy in a slightly more practical way. He set up the Owen L. Coon Foundation to direct his philanthropy and to consolidate his three major interests: educational advancement, service to the handicapped, and the Protestant church. This foundation was the brainchild of Owen and Carl L. Anderson, a fund-raising executive who met Owen during one of the war fund drives. Anderson was a smart, skilled organizer who impressed Owen immediately. He also shared many of Owen's beliefs about philanthropy and religion. Anderson was hired on January 1, 1946, to create the framework of the foundation.

The foundation was incorporated in Illinois on May 22, 1946. On June 1, five of the foundation's original board members—Owen, Louise, Harry Coon, Carl Anderson and Paul Morrison—met for the first time. Morrison was the Northwestern University finance professor who would meet Owen on Saturday mornings to offer business ideas. Eleanor was on the board, too, but she was not told about the first meeting. Nor was young Owen Coon Jr., who had not been named to the board.

The afternoon meeting, in the Coon house at 1201 Sheridan Road in Evanston, lasted about two hours. Owen was elected president, Anderson executive vice president and Harry vice president. The key to the foundation was, "To stimulate the entrance of increased numbers of high-minded individuals into the field of public service; to help the rehabilitation of handicapped persons, and to make the work of the church more effective."

These words sounded like boilerplate, but from the start the Coon Foundation was distinctive, articulating high-minded specific goals. The original religious, charitable, scientific, and educational purposes were:

1. To promote scientific research along lines for the alleviation of human suffering;

2. To care for the sick, aged, and helpless whose private resources are inadequate;

3. To conduct research for and otherwise assist in the improvement of living, moral, and working conditions;

4. To encourage social and domestic hygiene;

5. To encourage sanitation and measures for the prevention and suppression of disease;

6. To aid, provide or establish scholarships for deserving young men and women, and to aid and assist them in attending educational institutions;

7. To promote and aid in the mental, moral, intellectual, and physical improvement, assistance, and relief of the poor, indigent, or deserving inhabitants of the United States of America, regardless of race, color, or creed.

With so much on the agenda, it is surprising that the next meeting of the board was nearly a year later, on May 25, 1947. Three directors were added: Byron Coon; Harry's wife, Alma, and Eleanor's new husband, William Briggs. Briggs was a salesman who had worked for the Foote Cone and Belding advertising agency. He joined General Finance after his 1946 marriage to Eleanor and worked for the company in various capacities from salesman to executive until 1969, when he retired. He served on the Coon Foundation board until his death in 1987.

The board made its principles public in September 1947. In an article entitled "Owen Coon Establishes Remarkable Foundation," *Finance* magazine reported that Owen was following in the steps of the late Henry Ford, who had left his corporate voting stock to a foundation in order to create a philanthropic arm that would continue for decades after his death. "The foundation is so organized that in the event of Mr. Coon's death there will be no dissipation of stock values by reason of inheritance taxes," the magazine noted.

The fifty-three-year-old Coon, described by *Finance* as "still a vigorous and comparatively young man," had first assured an income for his family upon his death:

Having made adequate provisions for his family under a series of trusts, with the Coon family participating in no manner in the profits of the foundation, and with the foundation named as beneficiary under the terms of Mr. Coon's will leaving to it one-third of his GFC stock, the assurance of corporate longevity is complete. Moreover, the fact of the interlocking of boards of directors of the corporation and the foundation gives still further evidence that the future of the corporation will in no way be disturbed. A unique feature of the foundation is that the project will receive continuing support from Mr. Coon's purchase of substantial businesses of unquestioned integrity and character. These are turned over to the foundation, all profits from such enterprises being used in making grants to the causes or institutions chosen by the directors as being worthy of financial support.

*Finance* magazine reported that Owen had been inspired to create his foundation by a suggestion from his father. Then, in about 1935, Owen started dreaming about making it happen. But it was not until 1945 that Owen started doing research and outlining plans. In addition to supporting the Hardy Scholarships and Newton Fellowships, Owen wanted his money to go to the Chicago chapter of Goodwill Industries, a twenty-five-year-old West Side agency that taught physically and mentally handicapped people how to repair discarded items. Owen had served as the Chicago president of Goodwill, and served on the board of directors. *Finance* wrote that the Coon Foundation was different than others operating in the United States. "One marked feature is the matter of family interest and participation. Having made provision for the family through the trusts already mentioned, Mr. Coon took his family into account in the development of the entire foundation plan, to the point of organizing a family council which studies projects that might deserve support."

The *Evanston Review* explained that the family council would serve as an advisory board and that the board of directors would manage the foundation. A third group—advertising men, publishers, editors, public relations specialists, industrialists, social workers, business analysts, and others—would consider plans proposed by the family council before the plans were submitted to the directors for final action. "The general idea of this distinctive type of foundation, according to Mr. Coon, was conceived about ten years ago when he began to look ahead to the day when his family would be adequately provided for, when some portion of his business interests might be turned over to others and when he himself could give more of his time and effort to 'working for other people,'" the newspaper reported.

Owen told the reporter that the foundation would seek out projects rather than respond to solicitations, and would be highly focused in its grant giving. "In making gifts to multitudinous related projects a great deal of money can be frittered away," he said.

The *Review* provided the most detailed report of Owen's foundation. "While the Coon family plays an unofficial role, and has no part in the actual management of the foundation, it arrives at decisions and makes recommendations which serve as a guide for the board of directors in its operation of the enterprise," the paper explained. "This board, of which Mr. Coon is president, is composed of members of Mr. Coon's family and persons who are specialists in the various activities and duties pertinent to the foundation's over-all plan."

The family council started meeting informally from the start. They usually gathered on Sunday mornings at the Coons's home. Owen stressed the importance of those meetings to his children and their spouses, Harry and Alma Coon and Eleanor and Bill Briggs. (Owen Coon Jr. was still a minor.) Owen Sr. wrote to Eleanor in 1946: "There is also some action to be taken by the Owen L. Coon Foundation, of which both of you are directors (whether you knew it or not). It is important that the two of you attend such board meetings periodically in order to become familiar with the activities of the foundation, what it intends to do, and what your responsibilities are as directors."

Owen's plan was to endow his foundation with General Finance Corporation stock and then to find and buy companies in the foundation's name. He would use his proven strategy of finding firms in financial trouble and build them up. He figured he could keep the foundation growing on profits from these businesses instead of from an investment portfolio.

In September 1947, about 8,000 shares of General Finance Corporation stock was donated to the Coon Foundation. Then the foundation purchased a struggling company known as Intercontinental Engineers. The company became a division of the Coon Foundation, and the name of the company was changed to the O.L.C.F. Corporation, short for Owen L. Coon Foundation Corporation. Owen had expected to funnel all the profits from the engineering company directly into the foundation to avoid taxes, but government officials determined that company profits would not qualify for tax-exempt status. The foundation eventually paid all the taxes and penalties it made from the O.L.C.F. Corporation and liquidated the company.

‡    ‡    ‡    ‡

BY 1947, OWEN'S commitment to the Protestant church was becoming more tangible. Besides being a board member and finance chairman of Evanston's First United Methodist Church, Owen was president of the Methodist Social Union of Metropolitan Chicago and the Methodist Student Foundation of Northwestern. He also served as treasurer of the Midwest committee of the World Council of Churches. During the mid-forties, Owen came to believe that the bureaucracy of the Protestant church needed major reform. He was continually bombarded by charitable requests from Christian organizations that all worked on their own agenda.

That is why the Coon Foundation's first mission was to try to unify activities of various Christian organizations—primarily Protestant groups—to create a coordinated organization that would raise money and explain the significance and principles of Christianity.

The Rev. John Evans, writing in the *Chicago Tribune*, explained Owen's plans in October 1947.

> The principal project thus far launched is in the field of religion, where two objectives will be sought. These are the increasing acceptance of Christian ethical principles in the business world and in international affairs, and the unification of interchurch activities for the advancement of Christian standards, methods, and practices.
>
> In his announcement, Coon pointed to waste, duplication, and competition in the programs of the churches and to the churches' lack of an over-all

plan for fund raising. In this area, in particular, the foundation will seek increased cooperation between churches. Accordingly, the foundation will seek a more concentrated and better organized fund-raising program for churches and their related agencies.

Owen wanted to create a religious advertising and publicity program nationwide for advancing Christian principles, the *Tribune* reported. "In addition to the Coon family council and the foundation directorate, a group of experts is being formed and will be composed of foremost advertising men, publishers, editors, social workers, and educators," the newspaper wrote. The foundation published a thirty-two-page proposal in October 1947 suggesting that nine interdenominational Christian organizations consider merging into a new group that would be called the National Council of Churches of Christ in America.

The proposal was not a "rigid final offer or plan," but a call for Christian groups to start talking. It urged the merger of the Council of Church Boards of Education, Federal Council of the Churches of Christ in America, Foreign Missions Conference of North America, International Council of Religious Education, Home Missions Council of North America, Missionary Education Movement of the United States and Canada, United Council of Church Women, United Stewardship Council, and American Committee of the World Council of Churches.

As Owen pointed out, there were 233,000 Protestant churches and 634 church councils in the United States, all seeking support from 45 million Protestants as well as these nine national organizations. The result, he wrote, was that contributors received so many requests that they often did not know where their donations were going or if their gifts made a difference. He wrote that he and his foundation had been solicited by close to 100 Protestant agencies asking for support. Owen suggested that charitable solicitation for Protestant causes be centralized.

The foundation proposed that it would fund the new National Council of Churches of Christ in America so that it could conduct research into what the average person wanted out of religion. He also pledged to provide money so that it could better spread its message. "We would propose that the fund be great enough to tell this story through the use of modern mass media, that is, in local newspapers, national magazines, radio, television and the movies, to make an increasing acceptance possible of the doctrines of Christianity," the proposal stated.

The key, Owen believed, was to select and simplify the many messages promulgated by Christian churches. "There are great areas of the Christian message where there is no controversy," the proposal stated. "The contributions of Christianity to history, the need of men of faith in God, the service which the Church is rendering to millions and can give to millions more. These are but a few of the possible messages not now reaching 'the man in the street.'"

Owen knew that it would take at least two years to get the National Council of Churches off the ground. He committed his foundation to provide money until the council was operating on its own. "The foundation will acquire the entire ownership of a number of business institutions," the report stated. "Mr. Coon, because he believes his greatest genius is in business management for profit, will operate these business enterprises to make available the entire income for use by the Foundation. The first such businesses have already been acquired."

Owen wrote that his foundation's family council would help direct the foundation. "Mr. Coon, through this device, may train members of his immediate family, especially the second generation, in the policies, in the methods of operation, and in the ideals and purposes of the foundation, in order that in the event of his death (He is only fifty-three and in excellent health), the work of the foundation may be continued judiciously in the hands of the younger group," the foundation's proposal stated.

> The foundation has set as a major premise that of religious principles—and ethical principles—and to gain increasing acceptance in the everyday lives of men, in the business world and in the international field, which will come about only by acceptance of the principles of Christianity by an increasing number of people. It has therefore asked itself the question, 'How can religion and Christianity be made more effective?'

Coon felt it was crucial to unify the religions of Christianity to tell the story of Christianity's influence. "We must advance a step at a time," he stated. "But it is hoped this step may be taken toward a greater unity, a greater working together, a better understanding, giving to laymen of the Christian church some definite responsibilities carved out of the whole task, and where they will be wholly responsible, with advice of the clergy, for moving some phase of Protestant Christianity to greater service in the lives of men." The proposal concluded: "The Foundation now solicits suggestions from the agencies addressed and, it trusts, in time, their enthusiastic and wholehearted support."

During its first three years, the foundation was remarkably active. Carl Anderson traveled the country meeting with church officials to gain support for the foundation's plan, and Owen arranged his trips in order to talk to the leaders of major interdenominational organizations.

The early budgets of the Coon Foundation indicate just how much of a force Owen intended his foundation to become. In 1948, for example, the foundation spent $150,000, including $74,000 in salaries, $17,000 in officers' compensation and $5,000 in rent. The foundation gave $32,000 to the National Council of Churches of Christ for its planning committee, $13,000 to Goodwill Industries, $4,000 to the First United Methodist Church of Evanston, $2,000 to the Evanston War Memorial, $1,500 to the World Council of Churches, and $1,000 to the Methodist Student Foundation. That is quite a contrast to the foundation's first two budgets. In 1946, the foundation contributed a total of $22,000, including $8,000 to Goodwill, $6,000 to the First United Methodist Church, and $1,500 to the Evanston Community Fund. In 1947, the foundation made $18,000 in grants to 22 organizations, including $5,600 to Northwestern, $5,600 to the First United Methodist Church, $3,500 to Goodwill, and $1,750 to the Lake Bluff Orphanage.

The foundation's new mission was daunting. Wrote Carl Anderson to a newspaper in 1948: "The enclosed April 27th release is one in which your church-member readers will be interested. It is a brief account of what is probably the most significant movement in the history of Protestantism—the merger of interdenominational agencies into one central organization to be known as the National Council of the Churches of Christ in America. Our interest in the matter is that of providing funds with which to get the merger in operation and on its way. However, the Owen L. Coon Foundation seeks no publicity in this connection and we prefer to have the source of financial support unnamed."

‡　　‡　　‡　　‡

By 1947, auto financing had returned to the prewar peak. General Finance's annual report noted that the company financed one in every twelve car sales in the 26 cities it maintained offices. "In such manner, General Finance (and other progressive installment finance companies) are taking an important and essential part in raising American standards of living and in expanding the national economy," the report stated.

By then, General Finance had sold all of its manufacturing plants except for Climax Engineering. General Finance's five-year venture into manufacturing resulted in a $2 million profit. And in 1948, General Finance sold the Civic Opera House for a $1.7 million profit. Now the company would concentrate on its staples: auto and consumer financing.

Coon kept a torrid pace. In 1944, he wrote that he had spent the last five nights on a Pullman train. "Well—one gets used to many things in due course," he wrote.

"Owen Coon's working day is about sixteen hours long," *Time Sales Financing* magazine reported. "To him, work is play and he has never felt the need for any other hobby than business." Owen would wake up at 5:30 or 6 a.m. Then Alma or Harry would drive him to the commuter train, or he would head downtown in his seven-passenger chauffeured limousine. There, in the back seat, sat Owen, along with a box of papers, smoking cigars, working on the dictating machine. "I used to bitch at him," said Harry. "He would take a memo out of there, crumble it up and throw it out the window on the Outer Drive."

Owen didn't care about money—at least he didn't care about money to buy things. He craved money for what it could accomplish. His priority after the war was his work with religious institutions. He wrote to Carl Anderson on March 25, 1948, from the Gotham Hotel in New York: "I had a perfectly splendid meeting of the Board of Conferees today concerning the overall chart of organization and the campaign chart. There were a couple of suggestions made in the overall chart, which I know will have your concurrence, and a few suggestions were made concerning the presentation of the campaign organization chart. These suggestions were made in the line of strategy."

After purchasing Intercontinental Engineers in 1947 in the foundation's name, Owen bought eighty-acres of real estate in the Chicago suburb of Westchester with the intent of subdividing the property

130

and building twenty-four homes for sale. He was fearless and unflinching—and confident in making money wherever he turned.

In 1947, Owen was named to the board of Evanston's War Memorial when the city adopted a plan to build a remembrance to those who died in the two world wars. This same year, the Coon Foundation awarded the first Arthur W. Newton Fellowship, a $1,000 grant to graduate student R. Miller Upton, who would study consumer credit in finance companies and banks. This was also the year that Owen extended the Hardy Scholars to include Northwestern's law school students. And it was the year that Richard Briggs, Eleanor Briggs' third child, was born at Henrotin Hospital. Richard would later become president of the foundation.

‡    ‡    ‡    ‡

OWEN COON WAS A MAN who thought deeply about the passage of time, who sensed the falling dominoes of generations, who appreciated that he had been shaped by those who came before him and who fervently desired, in turn, to shape those who would follow. He thought deeply about his own mortality and was philosophical—he accepted it. But Owen was far too driven, far too involved in life, to dwell for long on death. He never talked to his children about such things, pushing ahead each new day. Although he suffered from a stomach ulcer and gallbladder problems, according to his life insurance records, he was never slowed by illness. He had too much to do.

Then came 1948. Early in the year, Owen was diagnosed with leukemia. He would die just months later in the heat of a Midwestern summer. And yet, until his last days, Owen kept working. He met with bankers to open new lines of credit. He met with church leaders to open new lines of communication. If he had to take his doctor along, he took his doctor along. When he couldn't walk, he was carried.

Owen's three children all vividly remember their father's last days.

Eleanor recalls watching him board a train to Kansas City to appear in a court case. He had promised his doctor that he would obey the doctor's orders if the doctor would accompany him on the trip. "He was taken to the train in an ambulance and put on the train in a stretcher," she remembered. "He slept in the lower berth; the doctor slept in the upper berth. He went to Kansas, went to the courtroom. He was dying, but went to the courtroom and settled the case."

Harry Coon recalls the day his father, though terribly frail, took a business trip to Clinton, Iowa. "I looked down at his hands, his fingernails," Harry said. "There was bleeding out of his fingernails. Orange blood. All the white corpuscles had started to eat away at him. I started to cry, and I'm not a crier. He said, 'Don't worry about it.' He gave me the story about life and death. He was philosophic. He came home and kept working. He didn't want to stop working. I can see him now sitting in that chair. He could hardly make it. He was getting paler and paler and thinner and thinner. In those days they didn't know much about leukemia."

And Owen Jr., the youngest child, recalls how his father, weeks before his death, insisted on flying to New York to finalize an important deal. Owen was taken to the airport in an ambulance. Upon his return, he was taken back to the hospital by ambulance. "It was pretty evident that he was going to die," Owen Jr. said. "At that time, there was no way to arrest it."

In the last weeks of Owen's life, Harry served as his father's driver, taking him around the city. "Every time we went over the slightest bump, I heard him cry," Harry said. "That broke my heart."

Eleanor was kept in the dark about her father's illness. She could see that he was sick, in and out of the hospital, but she had no idea that his condition was fatal. She recalls returning from a two-week vacation in midsummer and being told that he was in Henrotin Hospital. She rushed to see him. He dictated a letter to her and then said: "Why haven't they told you? Your father is dying."

Owen Coon died on August 2, 1948.

Harry, visiting a General Finance branch office in Dayton, Ohio, received word from Dr. John S. Ashby that he should rush home to see his father. Harry drove right to Henrotin Hospital and dashed up to his room, but found only a folded mattress. "I knew right away he was gone," Harry said. "They didn't have to tell me."

Owen Jr., out riding his motorcycle that night, chanced to smash it into the back of a parked car. He came home a bit banged up and, seeing his mother was not home, went to bed. The next morning, his mother told him that his father had died. As it happened, Owen had died just about the time of the crash.

# CHAPTER SEVEN

# The Foundation

---

"EVANSTON IS WHERE IT ALL STARTED—WHERE THE
MONEY CAME FROM—AND WHERE, IN MY OPINION, WE
SHOULD CONCENTRATE OUR EFFORTS AT THIS TIME."

Funeral services for Owen Lewis Coon were held on August 5, 1948, at the First United Methodist Church of Evanston. Dr. Ernest Tittle, Owen's friend and head of the church, officiated. Every pew was filled. Owen Jr. had never seen so many flowers. "Of course, I cried," he said. "I was at a tender age."

The *Chicago Tribune*, in its obituary, said the principal work of the Coon Foundation had been the merger of eight interdenominational councils of Protestant churches into a national council. (One of the original nine groups dropped out.) But Owen's National Council of Churches of Christ in America was far from a reality. "Associates of Mr. Coon announced yesterday the foundation has become self perpetuating and that its work will continue," the newspaper reported.

Public testimonials in the wake of Owen's death were eloquent. Friends and associates spoke glowingly of Owen as a business leader and as a man. "Owen Coon was a pioneer and a builder in the heroic American tradition," declared the Northwestern University Board of Directors in its memorial resolution. "He never enjoyed static situations—he was always seeking opportunities to build and expand organizations in business and philanthropy. He dreamed big dreams, and devoted himself almost fanatically to their attainment."

More poignant was a short exchange of letters between Owen's longtime attorney and friend, Dean Traxler, and Louise Coon. The day after Owen died, Traxler wrote: "You are the one person whom it is unnecessary to tell that Owen's passing has left a big void in a great many places. What most people who read the news will not know is that his capacity for friendship and his straightforward adherence to his objectives overshadowed even his business success; the world is really the poorer for his passing."

Louise replied a few weeks later, as she dutifully catalogued Owen's belongings for the settlement of his estate. "Here is the list of clothes," she wrote. "Not many as you know Owen wouldn't buy things for himself! Just a funny guy, but oh how I loved him—dirty shirt, unpolished shoes, egg on his tie and all. I hope you can read this list done in a few tears. As ever. Louise."

Those strong feelings toward Owen Coon and his memory remain to this day.

"He was such an elegant man," said Harry Coon, speaking more than fifty-five years after his father's death. "The years I spent with him after the war were the best years of my life. I think about them every day."

Owen's last will and testament was dated April 18, 1947. He gave all his jewelry, silverware, pictures, books, house and furnishings, clothing, automobiles, and other specific possessions to his wife. "All the rest of my estate," he wrote, "real and personal, wherever locate . . . I give and devise to the Owen L. Coon Foundation, an Illinois not for profit corporation."

Owen's will was standard, in a legal sense, but included a special letter of confidence concerning his brother, Byron Coon. Dated 1945 and addressed to the Northern Trust and Savings Bank, Owen wrote:

> From time to time in the past I have written to you expressing certain thoughts as to what your institution might consider doing in the event of my death to protect the investment in General Finance Corporation, from a management standpoint, represented by the stock of that company which is contained in various trusts established with your bank. ...My present thought is that in the event of my death the office of chairman of the board should be merged with that of president and that Byron S. Coon should function as both until such time as he thinks someone else should be made president and he assumes the office of chairman of the board alone. Byron has developed

very rapidly and in a wonderful manner in recent years and in the event of my death I am confident that the interests of my estate, evidenced by the stock of the company, would be safeguarded in a proper manner under his leadership. Should conditions change between now and the time of my death I will write you further.

At his death, Owen owned 88,897 common shares of General Finance Corporation stock. He also held 2,200 shares for his son, Owen Jr., and 65,550 shares in another Owen Coon trust. His estate was estimated at $510,000 in a petition filed in probate court. The estate did not include money in five trusts at the Northern Trust Company for Louise, Rose and Owen's three children, and did not include money in other trusts for his children and first wife, Alice. Through the trust funds he had established, he was able to leave all but his house and personal effects to the Coon Foundation. One newspaper reported: "Attorneys for the estate said Coon made ample provision for his wife; a daughter, Mrs. Eleanor Briggs, and two sons, Harry and Owen Jr., during his lifetime."

The estate that passed to Louise included the house on Sheridan Road and the Benson Avenue garage in Evanston; a house in Kankakee, Illinois; a garage in Champaign, Illinois; half interest in 1,560 acres of land near Walnut Ridge, Arkansas; twenty-five acres in Brazoria County, Texas, and other small lots in Illinois, Indiana, and Florida. It also included the nearly 89,000 shares of common stock in General Finance, 100 shares of common stock in Chicago National Bank, a 1947 DeSoto Club Coupe, and two oil wells in Wabash County, Illinois.

When he died, Owen owned thirty-nine life insurance policies with seventeen companies for a combined total of $667,500. He had carefully arranged that copies of all life insurance checks written during his last years would be held at his law office to prove that the policies were up-to-date.

‡    ‡    ‡    ‡

ON AUGUST 11, 1948, nine days after Owen's death, the stewards of his beloved foundation met once again. Louise Coon, Harry and Alma Coon, Eleanor and Bill Briggs, Paul Morrison, and Byron Coon gathered at the Orrington Hotel. Their first order of business was to pass a heart-felt resolution in memoriam of Owen L. Coon. It read:

> Whereas, a great tragedy, a great loss, a great sorrow has come to the Owen L. Coon Foundation in the death on August 2nd, 1948, of its beloved founder and president, and
>
> Whereas, his untimely and early passing has placed tremendous although joyous responsibilities on each of us to carry into fruition the program, high in purpose and helpfulness which he envisioned, and
>
> Whereas, this program now can only be consummated by those of us who remain and whom he has profoundly influenced by his way of life, his inspiration and his graciousness, therefore,
>
> Be it resolved, that all of us as a group and each and every one of us separately, solemnly, yet gladly accept the responsibility and challenge which has come to us and pledge our most sincere devotion, thought, and work to carry out the program of welfare for others for which he established this foundation.

The board voted to inscribe and bind the resolution. Each member of Owen's immediate family was to be given a copy. Then the board voted to appoint Paul Morrison, Owen's most trusted business advisor, as president of the foundation. Morrison was a nationally prominent budget advisor who had worked for thirty-five years as a professor of finance and director of the finance department at Northwestern's School of Commerce. "Morrison was chosen because he was older and had moxie," Harry Coon later said. "We all felt we needed his experience."

The following month, the board met at Louise's home on Sheridan Road to chart the foundation's future. Owen had envisioned a vibrant, strong, active foundation fueled by money he earned by purchasing and reviving businesses. Now, however, the foundation's financial situation was suddenly looking bleak. Without a steady stream of income, the board members knew the foundation's scope would have to be reduced drastically. Minutes from that meeting are terse:

> After discussion, it was the consensus of the meet-
> ing that the foundation maintain to the best of its
> ability the assistance it has offered in the unifica-
> tion of the Protestant church activities, but not
> to the extent of curtailing the educational and re-
> habilitation activities to which it was committed,
> nor impairing its financial structure.

The key was to cut staff expenses. Carl Anderson, who had worked brilliantly for nearly three years as the foundation's vice presi-dent, was asked to step down on October 1, 1948. The foundation awarded him an extra year's salary of $10,000.

In December 1948, the foundation met again, this time at By-ron's home in Kenilworth, Illinois, and voted to give $32,000 to the fledgling National Council of Churches, the group Owen and Carl An-derson were seeking to form.

Owen's religious endeavors flowered after his death. Although the present-day National Council of the Churches of Christ in the USA has not reshaped institutional Christianity to the degree that Owen and Anderson envisioned, it is a thriving organization comprised of 36 Prot-estant, Anglican, and Orthodox member denominations with more than 100,000 congregations and 50 million congregants. It presents itself as "the leading force for ecumenical cooperation among Christians in the United States," and may well be Owen's most enduring legacy.

Albert Gale, who served as the foundation's publicity director, best explained the fate of the foundation's church plan in the first few years after Owen's death. In a 1950 issue of the *Evanston Review*, he wrote:

> When the planning committee for the National
> Council of Churches announced recently that 'the
> year 1950 will be one of the great milestones of
> Christian progress,' it paid indirect tribute to a
> group of Evanston and Chicago businessmen, to an
> Evanston minister, and to a benevolent foundation

that has provided funds during the formative years of a movement that is said to mark 'another momentous forward step by American churches.' ...

The merger of interdenominational agencies into a single overall unit has been for many years a vision without action, other than the holding of occasional meetings and the issuing of progress reports. During this long period the project had been considered and postponed time and again.

Today, however, it has the official approval of twenty-five ecclesiastical bodies representing more than 26 million church members, and is the nearest approach to action that the Protestant churches of this country have ever achieved. Adherents to various creeds and traditions are proving that they can get together. What seemed to be impossible is being accomplished.

Gale was specific in crediting Owen's major role. "This is the story," he wrote, "of how a man's desire to do something worthwhile, outside the activities of his crowded business life, breathed energy into the undertaking and started it on a path that will end in full consummation when the National Council of the Churches of Christ in the USA comes into official existence at Cleveland next week."

Eight Protestant agencies, Gale continued, would soon lose their corporate identities in the merger:

This is a long step toward Protestant unity—probably the longest ever taken. Owen Coon passed away during the critical years when the foundation and the planning committee were working together on a program whose fruits will be seen next week when the constituting convention is held.

He will not be present when consummation becomes a fact. But those who worked with him, during the time when the pieces of a noble idea were being put together, will have great satisfaction in seeing this experiment in cooperative Christianity well started on its way.

Unfortunately, Owen Coon's sudden death at an early time in the formation of the National Council of Churches appears to have obscured his historic role. The organization's New York office has no official record of his work or the connection between the Coon Foundation and the National Council.

"Owen set up the committee that formed the National Council, but it turned out different than the foundation's desires," said Harry Coon. "The idea was to consolidate all the Protestant religions so that it would have more power—like the Catholic Church. Somewhere, somehow, the concept got lost—and we lost interest in the organization."

From the start, the organization took on a political tinge—taking liberal stands on such things as the death penalty, public school prayer, and South African apartheid. Owen wanted the group to stick to religion, helping to unify Protestant denominations and promoting the idea of Christianity. "The problem is that the group went down its own path," said Harry. "It did do away with much of the duplication and bureaucracy of the Protestant church, but then it went its separate way."

‡    ‡    ‡    ‡

OWEN'S FAMILY, trusted friends, and associates have headed the Owen L. Coon Foundation during its entire sixty-year history. Paul Morrison served as president from 1948 through 1961. Owen's son, Harry, succeeded him and served through 1991. And that year, Owen's grandson, Richard Briggs, took over.

Eleanor's children, Mary Ellen Segall, Richard Briggs, and Jean Latka, are on the board. Also on the board are Mary Ellen's son, William Segall, and his wife, Kimberly, as well as Jean Latka's husband, Thomas, and their daughter, Rose.

Owen's youngest son, Owen Coon Jr., joined the board soon after Owen's death, along with his first wife, Anne, and current wife, Suzanne Coon. (Anne Coon left the board following her divorce.) Owen

Jr.'s son, Owen "Trey" Coon III, and Trey's wife, Barbara, later joined the board. Two other family members, Owen's cousin and business associate Ray E. Titus and Louise's sister Pauline Dowdell, also have served on the board. Business associates and advisors include Harold Anderson, Hardin H. Hawes, Richard S. Oldberg, William S. Turner, Trowbridge "Toby" Callaway III, Arthur Schmehling, and Franklin W. Nitikman, who has served as board attorney for decades.

For several years after Owen's death and the $32,000 grant in 1948 to the National Council of Churches, the Owen Coon Foundation barely gave away any money. The foundation's board met three times in 1949 and handed out $5,000 to support the Hardy Scholarships, $125 to the Evanston Hospital Association, and $125 to the American Red Cross. The August meeting marked the beginning of divisions among board members. Byron Coon suggested that the foundation offer a $500 loan to G.K. Grabbe, the longtime treasurer of General Finance Corporation who had done substantial work setting up the foundation. The minutes read: "Byron S. Coon at this point stated that in his opinion one of the purposes of the foundation should be to assist worthy employees of GFC in such manner as is possible and is within the power of the foundation either by loaning funds to individuals or in some other manner."

Eleanor Briggs, among others, argued that Byron was taking the foundation in a direction never envisioned by Owen. "We had a horrible fight that night," she recalled. And she was suspicious that Byron would gain control by packing the board. "He was going to steal the foundation," she said. "I knew he would."

The fight set the stage for a long series of disagreements, continuing over years, about control of the board. "At one point, Louise wanted to fold the foundation because she did not want it to split the family, but she could not find any support," recalled Eleanor. In 1951, the board did consider turning over all the assets of the Coon Foundation to a charitable trust, but the idea never went beyond conversation. Byron supplemented the board's budget by donating General Finance Corporation money during the 1950s, but he eventually pursued his own philanthropy and distanced himself from the foundation. He resigned from the board in the late 1960s.

In 1950, the board voted to donate $600 to publish Dr. Tittle's sermons, agreed to settle a lawsuit, and voted to pay overdue taxes. That was the year that the federal government ruled that profits made by the foundation's subsidiary, Intercontinental Engineers, were subject to taxation. After paying the money, the foundation liquidated the company.

Except for the board fight over control, the 1950s were somewhat uneventful times for the foundation. Meetings were usually brief. Year after year, the foundation gave $5,000 to the Hardy Scholarships, $1,000 to the First United Methodist Church and $100 to local charities such as the Evanston Community Chest, Newberry Avenue Center, Evanston YMCA and American Red Cross.

Discussions at this time about the larger philosophy of the foundation usually arose when considering the Hardy Scholarships. The board determined during the early 1950s that the Hardy Scholars program would continue as a "quality" program rather than a "quantity" program. "It was felt that in this way Owen's wish that a better class of citizens be developed through this program would more fully be carried out," the minutes read.

In this era, the most promising Hardy Scholar was a top graduate of Northwestern University Law School named Daniel Walker. He was among the law school's very first Hardy Scholars. "The record of Daniel Walker to date is almost enough in itself to justify the whole program," James Rahl, the former Hardy Scholar who became a Northwestern Law School professor, reported to the board. "Walker was in such serious financial need that he might have had to leave school but for the Hardy cash awards, which he received supplementing his G.I. allowance. He was the outstanding man in his class all through school."

Walker graduated from law school in 1950, clerked for Supreme Court Chief Justice Fred M. Vinson and served on the U.S. Court of Military Appeals after being called to active duty as a Naval officer. "He is almost certain to carry the Hardy ideal to very high attainment," Rahl predicted.

That prediction proved to be accurate—but with a twist. Talented and industrious Dan Walker developed a populist image and was elected governor of Illinois in 1976. He served one term. But Walker later was convicted of federal crimes related to the financial mismanagement of several businesses. He served time in a federal prison in Duluth, Minnesota. Harry Coon would later call Walker "our infamous Coon Scholar."

‡     ‡     ‡     ‡

ESTABLISHED IN 1946 with about $600,000, the foundation's assets dropped to $250,000 by the early 1950s due to its early payouts for the

National Council of Churches and financial setbacks. It received yearly income from dividends, investments, real estate income, and an oil lease, but spent money on legal fees, life insurance, taxes and its grants and scholarships. In 1953, the foundation's principal was increased when Louise donated much of her real estate holdings. Later that year, the foundation received $115,000 from the Coon estate, boosting its net worth to $394,000. With money also coming in from the growth of General Finance, the foundation's assets bounced back in the mid- and late 1950s.

Starting in the 1960s, the foundation became more aggressive in making donations. In 1954, it set up a reserve fund at Northwestern University called the Owen L. Coon Foundation Fund, with an initial $25,000 grant. That fund would pool foundation money destined for future Northwestern projects.

The fund's first major endeavor was to make a grant of $100,000 to double the capacity of Northwestern University's Law Library, making it the nation's sixth largest. The new Owen L. Coon Library was dedicated in 1960. A year later, James Rahl, who was in the first Hardy class, delivered the keynote speech at a ceremonial unveiling of an oil painting portrait of Owen by artist William S. Schwartz. At the speech, Rahl recalled his last letter from Owen, received in early 1948:

> In it he charged me, as he often did with Hardy Scholars, in the most friendly but positive terms with being one of the 'links in the chain,' which he sought to forge between Professor Hardy and the world. ...I should like to say that I have never found that chain, which has steadily lengthened, to be at all a burdensome weight. But whenever you serve as a link in some kind of chain, you experience an occasional pull or tug, and this experience I find to be occurring more and more frequently as more Hardy Scholars are added to the chain.

Paul Morrison, who helped Byron Coon sort out Owen's estate and put the foundation on a sound financial basis, stepped down as president in 1961. In recognition of his service, the foundation donated $25,000 to Morrison's alma mater, DePauw University in Greencastle,

Indiana, to create a professorship in his honor. Harry Coon was named the foundation's new president.

Around 1960, the foundation began funding the Owen L. Coon Memorial Debate Tournament on the Northwestern campus. In the first years of the Coon tournament, the foundation annually gave Northwestern $1,000. Grants have increased as costs have increased; the foundation now donates $25,000 to help run the event. The three-day tournament, which attracts dozens of college teams, is considered one of the most prestigious invitationals in the nation, and has helped the Northwestern debate team become a national powerhouse. The team has won the National Debate Tournament, the college championship, thirteen times, including seven titles in the past twelve years. The team's headquarters, since 1980 called the Hardy House, displays paintings of Clarion Hardy and Owen Coon.

In 1964, board members and Northwestern officials signed a contract that called for the foundation to donate $1.25 million to construct a new school of speech, which was roughly half the estimated cost of the building. To be known as the Owen L. Coon Memorial Building, the structure was not to be built until the Owen L. Coon Foundation Fund, then at $369,000, grew to $1.25 million. At the same time, the contract called for construction before 1980.

In the mid-1960s, family members became concerned about the foundation's money in the Owen L. Coon Foundation Fund. As per agreement, Coon money placed in the fund had been invested in stocks by Northwestern as part of the Northwestern General Fund, and was therefore subject to the ups and downs of the market. Harry Coon, then president of the Coon Foundation, openly questioned the wisdom of Northwestern's investment strategy. The 1965 foundation annual meeting featured a "rather lively discussion," Harry wrote to Northwestern official Frank Kreml. "All of us have suddenly come to the realization of the remote possibility we might not realize our goal of $1.25 million."

Harry was financially conservative, apprehensive of the stock market. "Conceivably, we could make a total contribution of say a million dollars and wake up later and find it's worth only $800,000," Harry wrote. "The whimsy of the stock market, even with blue chips, concerns us greatly as to the overall advisability of continuing along on the same basis as we have in the past. The foundation's board would like to know as much as possible about the Northwestern General Fund as it can in order to base sound judgments as to future gifts."

The foundation's financial worries were reduced in 1968 when the Coon board agreed to sell 111,000 shares of General Finance Corporation stock to CNA Financial Corporation for $32 a share. CNA was in the process of taking over General Finance. The foundation received $3.55 million, greatly increasing its assets.

Harry Coon ran the foundation during the sixties, seventies, and eighties with the help of his wife, Alma. Harry and Alma had business experience from owning and running a small radio station, KWRE-AM, just outside of St. Louis in Warrentown, Missouri, during the fifties. After selling the station, Harry worked as a sales executive for WBBM in Chicago and, through his Harry H. Coon Productions, did the orchestrations for at least 150 commercials. He and Alma headed the foundation strictly as volunteers and brought a passion to the job, as well as a distinct point of view. They watched every dime. "We wanted to put money into things that would create more money and have an impact," he said. "When I saw what you can create with seed money, I became excited."

After Harry took over as president, he sold all the foundation's stock and real estate investments, and put the money into bonds and government paper. "It's amazing how the money accumulated," he said. He pushed hard to keep the foundation out of the stock market because he considered it too risky. He butted heads for years with Bill Turner, vice president of Northern Trust, which still helps oversee the foundation's assets. "Bill is a friend, but he criticized me for my investment strategy," Harry said. "I didn't want to follow Northern's advice—putting money in such things as Japanese stocks. I took advantage of high interest rates, and I said, 'To hell with equities.' That was our big fight with the banks. I was adamant about it, and I'm glad I stuck to my guns. To this day, I know I was right."

Toby Callaway, who served as a portfolio manager at Northern Trust during the sixties and seventies, worked closely with Harry Coon on investments. After leaving the bank, Callaway served on the Coon Foundation board of directors until his death in 2004. He said that Harry and Alma Coon became especially worried about the foundation's stock position in 1973-74, a particularly bad time for the market. Harry liquidated the entire portfolio.

"It is generally accepted that a foundation or individual portfolio will embrace at least 50 percent in stocks," Callaway said. "Harry's view was fairly uncommon. Harry and Alma believed that any tiny bad news meant we were going to hell in a handbasket. I tried to resist this trend, but it was a hopeless cause. With inflation on the rise during the 1970s, it was easy for the foundation to earn more than 5 percent"—an attractive alternative to the stock market.

Harry's decision to withdraw from the stock market helped the foundation plow through the dismal financial years of the 1970s. But he missed the start of the market's remarkable long run up the ladder in the 1980s. Since Harry stepped down as president in 1991, the foundation has moved back into the market. It now maintains about 45 percent of its portfolio in stocks. The average percentage for a foundation of this size is about 60 percent. "We may eventually get there," Callaway said in 2004. "We are inching higher and we are getting more venturesome."

‡　　‡　　‡　　‡

BY THE LATE SIXTIES, several members of the board began reassessing the Coon Foundation's commitment to the Hardy Scholars program. Campus unrest had dampened the foundation's determination to help college students pay their way through Northwestern. Harry and Alma, in particular, were disgusted by the appearance and outlook of hippie students on campus. They steered the board to a new strategy. The board started putting more of its money behind bricks-and-mortar projects and scientific research to keep out of the emerging political mainstream. The foundation had been granting about $40,000 a year to support undergraduate and law school Hardy Scholars through much of the sixties. "The family feels, and justifiably I think, the cost of the Hardy program to the foundation has reached unrealistic proportions and should be brought in line to $30,000 annually," Harry wrote to Northwestern in 1968. "We'd like to cap it at this figure by the end of fiscal year 1971."

Beginning in 1969, the board started contracting its scholarship funding, paying out $35,000 to the Hardy programs in 1969, $31,000 in 1970 and $30,000 in 1971 and 1972. On November 17, 1970, at an informal meeting of family members attended by Harry and Alma Coon, Eleanor and William Briggs, Owen Coon Jr., and Louise Coon, the board voted to end its support of the Hardy Scholarships program. The decision, after 35 years of Hardy Scholarships, was precipitated by a small request from the School of Speech for extra money to cover transportation expenses for debaters.

> After due consideration by the family members present and pending ratification by the directors of the Owen L. Coon Foundation, it was decided, for a number of reasons, to deny their request and to also bring about the termination of the Hardy Scholarship program in both the School of Speech and the School of Law altogether, and to notify each school of our intentions at the propitious time, making sure each school does not commit itself to additional Hardy applicants.

In 1971, the board passed a resolution to officially phase out the Hardy Scholars law school scholarship program at the end of the 1972-73 school year. The law school was Harry's main target. "These schools openly admit they are communist, that they are Maoist," said Harry in a 2004 interview. "I resented the way the law school was going. Jim Rahl had filled the school with liberals—it was becoming socialist. Owen Coon would have spun around many times in his grave knowing that we were supporting that school. I had many arguments with Jim, and I told him that I thought his school was hurting society."

Harry retained his personal affection for James Rahl, who became dean of the Northwestern Law School, but Harry differed sharply with his politics. "It wasn't just Jim and the law school," said Harry. "I saw the whole educational establishment from coast to coast turning socialistic and it hurt me. I'm upset about where America is going. You think Rush Limbaugh is conservative? You haven't met me."

The Hardy Scholars program at the law school was disbanded, but the Hardy Scholars program for undergraduates continues to this day. The Coon Foundation stopped annual payments to the undergraduate scholarship program in 1974, but—unbeknownst to the foundation for decades—scholarships continue to be provided from the original endowment fund. The C. D. Hardy Scholarship Fund and the Owen L. Coon Fund for Hardy Scholars, both originally set up by the foundation, grant seven to ten undergraduate scholarships of $5,000 to $10,000 each year. The two funds have more than $1.5 million in assets.

Hundreds of Northwestern students have benefited from the Hardy scholarship program. Among them are Sander Vanocur, White House correspondent and national political correspondent for NBC-TV and senior correspondent for ABC-TV; Don H. Reuben, senior partner in the Chicago law firm of Reuben & Proctor; Earl E. Pollock, partner in the Chicago law firm of Sonnenschein Nath & Rosenthal; Austin Ranney, resident scholar with the American Enterprise Institute in Washington, D.C.; Richard M. Marcus, a state appellate judge in Ohio; Harry Wappler, chief meteorologist with KIRO-TV in Seattle, Washington; Mike Morris, general counsel of Sun Microsystems in Santa Clara, California; and Stephan Thernstrom, professor of history at Harvard University.

Instead of Hardy Scholars, the foundation agreed to fund a new medical fellowship program at Northwestern University Medical School. Called Owen L. Coon Foundation Scholars, two or three medical school residents a year received money so that they could continue their research for another year. The program ran from the early 1970s to the mid-1980s. "I bet we put through 40 of the best doctors in the fellowship program," said Harry Coon. "The results are great. We see doctors all over the country at the top of their profession. I am proud of the people who went through this program."

In 1969, the Coon Foundation voted to make its first major donation in decades to a non-Northwestern facility. The board voted to establish an endowment to fund the Louise W. Coon Chair in Medicine at Evanston Hospital. The chairman of the Evanston Hospital department of medicine holds the chair. It was the first donation not made in Owen's name. Said Harry: "As far as I was concerned, it was always Owen L. Coon, Owen L. Coon, Owen L. Coon. The only change we made was when we made the first chair at Evanston Hospital. It was made to recognize Louise, my mother. I was so happy we did that."

Later that year, Byron Coon and Paul Morrison resigned as directors of the Coon Foundation. They submitted their resignations partly because they disagreed with the direction of the foundation and because they were scaling back their public lives. They both also resigned as directors of General Finance Corporation that year. Byron, in a handwritten note from his home in Fort Lauderdale, Florida, said he would no longer be in Evanston in the winter, which would make it difficult to give the foundation the proper attention. "It seems to me that over the years I have made ample contributions to the growth in the assets of the foundation and have fulfilled my responsibility to Owen's memory and to his family."

In 1973, the foundation and Northwestern scrapped their old plans for a new School of Speech, deciding instead to use the $1.25 million building fund for three other worthy purposes on campus. They were:

> —The Owen L. Coon Forum, a lecture-discussion center on the Evanston campus. The foundation agreed to pay $500,000 toward the $1 million building to be shared by the Graduate School of Management and School of Education. The building linked the Graduate School of Management's Leverone Hall to the School of Education Building.

> —The Owen L. Coon Professor of Psychiatry, an endowment of $500,000 for the school of medicine. That position went to Dr. Harold M. Visotsky, department chairman and director of the Northwestern Institute of Psychiatry.

> —The Owen L. Coon Professor of Law, an endowment of $500,000 to the School of Law. Despite Harry Coon's misgivings, that position went to James Rahl, dean of the law school.

Northwestern and the foundation agreed to the changes, but legal work was neccessary to make them possible. "To make a long story short, we changed horses and funded the forum and two chairs instead," Harry later wrote. "If I recall, in order to accomplish this, Northwestern had to bring a lawsuit against the foundation, haul in the attorney general of Illinois, and additional legal bills were incurred on both sides."

In 1978, the overall assets of the foundation reached $3.8 million. That year, the board voted to donate $325,000 for a new $500,000 cardiac cauterization laboratory at Evanston Hospital. The lab would help identify and diagnose heart ailments.

In 1979, the Coon Foundation voted to spend $900,000 to build a modern laser research laboratory. "This is one of the most exciting prospects the Owen L. Coon Foundation has ever considered," Harry wrote. The money was used by Northwestern to add one story to the planned annex of Technological Institute at 2145 Sheridan. The lab, which opened in 1981, was considered the best laser lab in the world at the time, and was the largest in the nation. It helped Northwestern draw an average of $1.2 million a year in outside grants in the eighties and continues to operate. "Here is another project in which others are contributing funds and will continue to do so and 'Coon' is on the door," Harry wrote. "To be a part of the 'key' within a technology that will no doubt change the way in which future generations will live is an exciting prospect."

In 1981, the foundation gave $200,000 to Evanston Hospital to create the Owen L. Coon Ocular Diagnostic and Treatment Center, a comprehensive eye care facility at the hospital. After approving the treatment center, the board voted for no other large grants for several years. But with foundation assets of almost $5.1 million in 1987, Harry Coon told board members it was time to make some long-term plans. The foundation settled on three major projects:

> —$1 million to Northwestern to endow a chair in molecular biology on the Evanston campus. Dr. Emanuel Margoliash was selected the first Owen Coon Professor of Molecular Biology. His studies helped scientists understand the immune system.

> —$1 million to Evanston Hospital to build a research laboratory floor in a new $23 million, six-story building.

> —$1 million to Northwestern for the construction of a new medical research and educational building on the Chicago campus. The money was to help build a $47.5 million, sixteen-story structure at northeast corner of Fairbanks Court and Superior Street. Northwestern promised to name research suites in the new building for Owen Coon.

Because of these major commitments, the foundation decided to end the medical fellowships. Harry Coon wrote Dr. Harry N.

Beaty, dean of Northwestern University Medical School, on June 22, 1987:

> This is one of those good news, bad news letters. First, the bad news. The board, at our annual meeting this past Friday, June 19th, made the thoughtful decision to end funding of the Owen L. Coon Fellowships in Medicine. Now that you're over the shock, the good news is the foundation has decided, over a period of 8 to 10 years, to grant Northwestern the sum of $2 million—$1 million toward the construction of a new medical research and education building on the Chicago campus and $1 million to endow a chair in molecular biology on the Evanston campus.

By the late 1980s, another split was developing on the board. Eleanor Coon was determined to spend all, or almost all, of the foundation's money on Northwestern. Harry and Alma Coon, along with Louise, favored spending some foundation money at Evanston Hospital. Harry said that he was not as interested in "bricks and mortar projects" as he was in endowing professorships.

The split became so rancorous that in 1987 Louise once again suggested dissolving the foundation. Because she hated that the family was arguing bitterly over foundation spending, she suggested creating a trust. Eleanor opposed the idea, however, and Harry insisted he would never approve of dissolving the foundation without unanimous consent.

On August 14, 1987, Harry Coon wrote a letter to Richard Briggs that discussed the split in philosophy among the board members:

> I do not want to take part or underwrite any of the labs downtown. It's no deal for us, as there is absolutely no visibility or payoff for us at all. The chair in molecular biology in the College of Arts and Sciences on the Evanston campus is excellent. As you know, this is part of 'The Great Teachers Program' of which your mother has played an ac-

tive role. This would give us the same effective results as the chairs in Law and Psychiatry.

Now let me say this to you. At the last meeting, your mother expressed the feeling that Evanston Hospital was of no interest to Owen Coon. Eleanor is forgetting that the foundation was started by Louise and Owen, and that Louise has every right, and with respect to her, to have some programs carried through that are of her choosing so long as they come within the parameters of the Foundation's charter.

Take a good look at the Evanston Hospital proposal. It has everything going for it. 33,500 square feet, its own front entrance and great visibility which the labs downtown do not have. The Northwestern labs amount to seven closets down the hall on the forth floor of the new medical building. Here is another valid reason why we did not favor participation in the addition to the law library. The name Coon was already there.

Evanston is where it all started—where the money came from—and, in my opinion, is where we should concentrate our efforts at this time.

Richard replied to Harry that he and his mother agreed on the $1 million for the research center at Evanston Hospital and the $1 million for the Northwestern University research center. "If you and [Northwestern University President] Arnold Weber believe that the chair in molecular biology is in the best interest of both Northwestern and the Foundation, please proceed." (The board later voted to give the $1 million grant for the Evanston Hospital research center, but did not vote to give the $1 million grant for the Northwestern center.)

At the 1991 annual meeting, Harry Coon announced to the board that he wanted to step down as president. He did not specify his reasons, but the decision came at the end of several difficult meetings at which Harry and Alma constantly seemed to be at odds with Eleanor and Owen Jr. Also, Harry was being criticized for his conservative investment strategy. Stock trading had come back into fashion, yet he still wanted no part of it. And Harry had private considerations. He had developed an interested in Colonial Williamsburg, Virginia, near where he was restoring a 1732 mansion. "I asked if anybody else wanted the job, and Dick Briggs said he did," Harry recalled. "Finally I told [foundation attorney] Frank Nitikman, 'I want Dick to be president.'"

Eleanor recalls that Harry said he would stay around for a year to help his replacement. However, a few days later, Harry, Alma, and Louise submitted their resignations. Harry acknowledges he had agreed to remain active on the board for another year, but says he soon realized it would be better to make a clean break. "My interest was down in Virginia then," he said. "I was restoring this house with Alma and we had a lot of friends there. This was fun, and I wanted to play."

Richard Briggs called a special meeting to elect officers to fill the vacancies. The meeting was held on September 6, 1991, at the Skokie Country Club in Glencoe. Owen Coon Jr., who refused to be considered for the post, nominated Richard to the office of president. Richard was unanimously elected.

The board honored the dedication shown by Harry, Alma, and Louise by passing a resolution thanking them for their work. But the board made it clear that it was seeking a new path by passing a resolution that read, "The directors unanimously agreed that Northwestern University should continue to be the primary recipient of the foundation's contributions. Evanston Hospital may also continue to be considered as a recipient, but no decisions regarding funding are necessary at this time due to pending commitments."

The following year, the board created a projects committee to evaluate new proposals and appointed Eleanor Coon as chairman. The committee met with Northwestern officials and received four proposals, which it narrowed to two. In 1993, the board voted to donate $1 million to establish the Owen L. Coon Endowed Scholarship Fund for undergraduates. The program was in keeping with the vision of Northwestern President Arnold Weber, who launched a $60 million campaign fund for student scholarships.

The Coon Scholarship Fund, in keeping with Owen's original idea of raising the moral standards of college students, requires scholarship winners to perform voluntary service in metropolitan Chicago for at least forty hours per quarter. The students, known as Owen L. Coon Scholars, receive a minimum of $5,000 per year. The first Coon Scholar, Kathleen Lavin, was chosen in 1993. At the dedication of the program, Richard Briggs again recalled Owen's vision. "Today, through this endowed scholarship fund, we will establish new links in the chain," he said. "It is my fervent hope that by this program we will attract students who may not have come to Northwestern University otherwise, who will fully appreciate the tremendous education Northwestern provides, and will share with others what they receive."

Northwestern University agreed to match the foundation's $1 million grant with $1 million to $2 million in other grants. Northwestern President Weber wrote the family: "It has been said by historians that great private universities in America are sustained by great families over the course of their development. The relationship between the Coon Family and Northwestern is certainly emblematic of that fact and it has become, in many ways, a hallmark of the University's success in the twentieth century."

By 1993, the foundation's assets exceeded $6 million for the first time. In 1995, Richard Briggs asked Northwestern Law School officials to submit a proposal to honor James Rahl, who had died the previous year. The foundation donated $250,000 in 1997 to endow the James A. Rahl/Owen L. Coon Senior Research Program. The program, which was begun by Rahl years earlier, encourages third-year law school students to do original research on legal issues. The foundation scholarships, given to dozens of students per year, fund this research.

On the fiftieth anniversary of the Coon Foundation in 1996, the board met at the Skokie Country Club, a favorite meeting site since Richard Briggs was elected president in 1991. "Eleanor spoke about Owen and Owen Coon Jr. spoke about his mother, who passed away during the past year," the minutes read. At that meeting, the foundation discussed resurrecting the James S. Coon Scholarship program to provide money to students at Rantoul High School students who want to attend Northwestern. The $1,000 that Owen had placed into a Northwestern fund in 1944 for a "deserving boy" had rarely been touched and had grown to $20,000. Since then, the foundation has voted to increase the size of the fund from $20,000 to $100,000.

In 1998, the foundation further returned to Owen Coon's roots by voting to endow the $1 million Owen L. Coon Professorship of

Argumentation and Debate and endow the $200,000 Owen L. Coon Fund for Public Debate. The first Coon Professor of Argumentation and Debate was David Zarefsky, a former Hardy Scholar who had spent his entire undergraduate and graduate years at Northwestern and taught there ever since. He became a full professor in 1982, associate dean in 1983, and served as dean from 1988 until 2000.

In total, the foundation started two Hardy Scholarships programs, the Newton Fellowship, the Coon Endowed Scholarships, and the James S. Coon Scholarships at Northwestern. Moreover, the foundation has set up six chairs at Northwestern University and Evanston Hospital.

—The Louise W. Coon Chair in Medicine was established in 1970 as the first endowed chair in the history of Evanston Northwestern Healthcare. Dr. Leonard Jourdanais held the chair from 1970 to 1974, Dr. Thomas Killip held it from 1974 to 1979, Dr. E. Stephen Kurtides from 1979 to 1998, and Dr. Janardan Khandekar holds the chair now.

—The Owen L. Coon Chair in Psychiatry (now called the Coon Professorship in Psychiatry and Behavior Sciences) was started in 1973 with an initial gift of $500,000. An additional $500,000 in interest has been added to the account over the years. Harold Visotsky held the chair from 1974 to 2002. He has since been replaced by Professor of Psychiatry Linda A. Teplin. She also serves as the director of the Psycho-Legal Studies program at the Northwestern University Medical School.

—The Owen L. Coon Chair in Law at Northwestern University was held by James Rahl from 1974 to 1988. He was followed that year by John P. Heinz, who still holds the chair.

—The Owen L. Coon Professorship in Molecular Biology was held by Emanuel Margoliash from

154

1988 to 1990, by James Douglas Engel from 1990 to 2002, by Alfonso Mondragon from 2002 to 2004, and is now held by Richard Carthew.

—The Owen L. Coon Professorship in Argumentation and Debate has been held by David Zarefsky since it was established in 1998. The foundation established the chair in the School of Speech, now called the School of Communication.

—The Owen L. Coon Chair in Cardiothoracic Surgery at Evanston Northwestern Healthcare was held by Dr. Todd K. Rosengart when it was established in 2003 with a $1.5 million pledge. Rosengart, head of the hospital's division of cardiothoracic surgery, stepped down at the end of 2005. Dr. John C. Alexander has been appointed his succesor.

‡ ‡ ‡ ‡

GENERAL FINANCE, Owen Coon's great business creation, has thrived. Its "Friendly Bob Adams"—a smiling face logo and radio voice symbolizing the company's neighborly service—helped boost company sales in the 1950s as Americans migrated to the suburbs and purchased cars as never before. In 1945, General Finance had forty branch offices, 286 employees and boasted a net worth of about $7 million. Ten years later, the company had 130 branch offices, 1,021 employees and a net worth of $19 million. Ten years after that, the company had 375 branch offices, 2,323 employees and a net worth of about $42 million.

Considerable credit must go to Byron Coon, who served as chairman of the board and president for almost two decades after Owen's death. And considerable credit must go to Owen himself, who hired almost all the executives and directors who continued to manage the company. Among them were Ray Titus, who eventually was named president, and top officials Richard J. Trenkmann, Paul H. Brown, and E. F. Wonderlic, who moved the corporate headquarters to Evanston in 1956. General Finance was acquired by CNA Financial in 1968. It has subsequently been sold, and now exists as American General Finance, based in Evansville, Indiana. The company no longer has any direct connection to the Coon family.

Rose Coon, Owen's mother, died at Wesley Memorial Hospital in Chicago in 1961, at age eighty-eight. She was buried in Oak Grove Cemetery in LeRoy, Illinois, near her husband, James Coon.

Alice Wright Coon, Owen's first wife, died at St. Mary's Hospital in Kankakee, Illinois, on March 22, 1976, at age seventy-nine. She was buried in Elmwood Cemetery in Kankakee. Her lawsuit contesting the 1929 divorce was settled in 1950 with the Coon estate agreeing to pay Alice an extra $40,000.

Byron Coon, Owen's brother, died in Fort Lauderdale, Florida, in 1986, at age eighty-three after a long illness. Byron's family received a reported $7.1 million after his death. He was buried in Memorial Park Cemetery in Skokie, Illinois.

Louise Dowdell Walker Coon, Owen's second wife, died in the McGaw Health Center of the Presbyterian Homes in Evanston on April 15, 1996, at age ninety-five. She, too, was buried at Memorial Park Cemetery in Skokie, near Owen.

The Hardy Scholarships program still exists at Northwestern University. In its seven decades of existence, the program has provided hundreds of scholarships.

The Owen L. Coon Foundation celebrates its sixtieth anniversary in 2006 with assets of about $8 million. Owen's three children—Eleanor Briggs, Harry Coon, and Owen Coon Jr.—carry on his vision and his legacy. They have given away millions of dollars and made dreams possible for thousands of people. And now they have passed down the leadership of the foundation to their children—Mary Ellen Segall, Richard Briggs, Jean Latka, and Owen Coon III—and their children's children as well as close friends.

A twentieth century story of success and service has moved into the twenty-first century: From Owen Coon to Owen Coon's children to Owen Coon's grandchildren to Owen Coon's great-grandchildren.

The links in the chain are unbroken.

# Afterword

O n one level, this book was written to show how an American dreamer, Owen L. Coon, created a fortune from various car and credit businesses. On another level, this book was written to expose the complexity of that American dream. Owen Coon's rags-to-riches story has a complicated face. The dream of wealth—so easily seen in the billboards across America that portrayed a family with its own shiny Model T Ford—had a second face. Middle America needed credit to purchase the dream. The desire for wealth and the credit agencies that met that desire are all part of the backbone of American history. While the story of the American dream has always been recognized as a myth only a few can enjoy (as Martin Luther King Jr. stated, when the black man goes to cash his checks for American opportunity, the check is declared void), through Owen Coon we see an instance of the dream come true.

On a more personal level, the use of wealth and of credit was also a source of contention. Controversy between Owen and his first wife and daughter often centered on spending versus a certain iron-edged discipline. This tension is part of the irony of American dreaming. The American dream is about self-made wealth; yet, it is reliant on others in a complex system of credit dependencies. Thus, this biography of Owen Coon is both a personal story and a public document of a time period—charting the complexity of American dreaming.

This book also steps beyond the economic dream. It reveals how the myth of the American dream is also a story about how Americans identify themselves—a certain American mythos. What is an American? During this time period, there developed a certain identification of being American, buying products, and receiving credit—what Lendol Calder calls a type of "love affair." This love affair with cars and credit also fostered certain moral and economic identities. Private, public, and political disputes arose over how to identify with money and products amidst historical upheavals, such as the Depression and world wars. What this biography offers is a paradigm of American identity—wrapped up in ideas about how to spend money, how to live ethically, and how to recover and build during and after war.

Chapter One elucidates how certain public memories of the past haunt the American mind. Perhaps the Great Depression will always be the darkest memory, because it represented the death of the American dream. In 1932, unemployment reached 14 million and the national income had fallen by 50 percent. It is intriguing that our story begins with Owen Coon's sense of transformation during this time of economic crisis. Owen's letters to his mentor at Northwestern University imply that Owen's agnostic uncertainty was replaced by a vision, a quotidian ethic of everyday living.

Focusing on the twenties and thirties, the second chapter remembers the Great Depression. This era was also the Age of Jazz. The era of jazz and the time of economic crisis seem completely at odds with one another; yet, the giddy jazz age suggested that love and prosperity seemed to fit together. And the mythical dream of American prosperity, which driving a car epitomized, occurred even as people cashed checks for cars, the checks bounced, and the car became part of the dream deferred. Linking the public and private, Owen Coon built his financing company from this dream that every American desires a car. At the same time, Owen became anxious that his wife Alice would ruin their credit with her extreme spending and hiding of the bills. In a love story straight out of Fitzgerald's *The Great Gatsby*, we see the anxiety and marriage crisis enmeshed in the economic love affair with credit.

In both public and private settings, Chapter Three shows Owen as a man of vision who desired control. The first thing he did when he took over the General Finance Corporation was to fire all the officers, putting an end to the organization's politics and dramatically increasing its profits. Not only did Owen make a profit during the Great Depression, he also supported other visionaries, such as Professor Paul Schilpp, whose position on pacifism was not popular. The need to control credit and consumption—ghostly presences that haunted Owen's first marriage—returned to haunt the newly blended families. Owen Coon, greatly devoted to his daughter, stated that he had only "one primary goal" in raising her. Namely, to make sure she did not grow up like her mother as far as the spending of money. Part of the complexity of Owen Coon is seen in his grand vision for change and his risk-taking, positioned beside his desire for control, even over his family. How does this illuminate the post-World

War I times? Perhaps the desire for spectacular wealth and the apprehension of credit prove uneasy bedfellows.

During World War II, as we see in Chapter Four, many of the young men who were offered scholarships at Northwestern University found themselves deciding between college and military commitments. Many scholars were drafted from Northwestern, and at one point the campus functioned as a "virtual naval base" before the returning GIs started enrolling in vast numbers after the war. This World War II era is also characterized by a change in the amount of government regulation and control over credit companies. The Internal Revenue Service, constantly analyzing the ebb and flow of Owen's credit company, started questioning his corporate tax returns just before the war. A settlement in 1942 allowed Owen to maintain his perfect credit reputation. American identity, as seen in this particular case, is preoccupied with war, money, and the potential dreams and consequences of credit.

The fifth chapter examines how the force of the war was felt everywhere, even at Northwestern, where 400 faculty members were granted leaves of absence for the armed forces or related war projects. During the war years, economics was often at the heart of Owen Coon's vision for family and national life. Issues of trust and trust funds, spending, and responsibility were central to his choices during World War II. On a public level, he made speeches to raise funds for the war, and he gave loans for industries to produce bomb parts. On a private level, he used strict economic logic to advise his daughter during crisis. He shifted the focus of credit from driving the American dream to driving the American war machine.

In Chapter Six, we see Coon's post-war vision for an expanded car market come true. He also funded economic consolidation for the National Council of Churches and revised his vision of scholarships at Northwestern, imagining funds for a (male) political figure. Owen Coon died in 1948. The final chapter chronicles the choices—and disputes—of various foundation members. In the foundation's sixty years, hundreds of Northwestern students have received scholarships, forming even more links in the American chain.

KIMBERLY SEGALL

MEMBER, OWEN L. COON FOUNDATION

ASSOCIATE PROFESSOR, SEATTLE PACIFIC UNIVERSITY

# Contents of the Appendix

APPENDIX                                                                PAGE

Chronology  .   .   .   .   .   .   .   .   .   .   164
Principal Grants  .   .   .   .   .   .   .   .   168
Hardy Scholars  .   .   .   .   .   .   .   .   170
Owen L. Coon Scholarship Recipients  .   .   .   .   178
James S. Coon Scholars  .   .   .   .   .   .   .   180
Owen L. Coon Fellowships in Medicine  .   .   .   181
Rahl/Coon Senior Research Participants  .   .   .   182
Owen L. Coon Foundation Directors  .   .   .   .   186

# Chronology

---

**May 1, 1866:** James S. Coon, Owen Coon's father, born in Higginsville, Illinois.

**December 16, 1872:** Rose O. Rike, Owen's mother, born in LeRoy, Illinois.

**April 7, 1892:** James Coon marries Rose Rike in LeRoy.

**July 1, 1894:** Owen Lewis Coon, the couple's first son, is born in Rantoul, Illinois.

**April 2, 1903:** Byron Samuel Coon, the couple's second son, is born in Rantoul.

**1909:** Owen takes a grand tour of Europe with Rose following his freshman year at Rantoul High School.

**1912:** Owen graduates from Rantoul High School and enters Northwestern University.

**1915:** Owen graduates from Northwestern University with a bachelor's degree from the College of Liberal Arts. He enters Northwestern University Law School.

**1917-18:** Owen takes a year off from law school to operate a farm in Two Buttes, Colorado.

**1918:** Owen passes the bar examination and briefly enlists in the Navy. His parents move to Evanston, Illinois.

**May 22, 1918:** Owen marries Alice Elizabeth Wright in Evanston.

**1919:** Owen graduates from Northwestern University Law School.

**1919-1924:** Owen practices law in downtown Chicago.

**February 3, 1921:** Eleanor Rose Coon, Owen and Alice's only child, is born.

**March 1, 1925:** James and Owen form a partnership called the Evanston Motor Acceptance Company. (The firm changed its name to the Motor Acceptance Company in 1928.)

**August 19, 1929:** Owen divorces Alice. Divorce decree entered in Cook County Superior Court.

**March 22, 1930:** Owen marries Louise Dowdell Walker in Evanston.

**January 21, 1932:** Owen Coon Jr., Owen and Louise's only child together, is born.

**1933:** Owen and Louise move from Evanston to 150 Park Avenue in Glencoe.

**June 23, 1934:** Owen signs a contract to run the Detroit-based General Finance Company and serve as president.

**December 18, 1934:** Owen files a petition to adopt Louise's son, Harry Harold Walker. He takes the name Harry Harold Coon.

**1935:** Clarion Dewitt Hardy Scholarships in Forensics are established at Northwestern University.

**December 2, 1935:** Motor Acceptance Company officially merges with General Finance Corporation.

**1936:** Owen is nominated to sit on Northwestern University's Board of Trustees.

**1936:** General Finance Corporation shares are traded on the Chicago Stock Exchange for the first time.

**1937:** Owen is appointed president of the American Finance Conference. (He was reelected in 1938.)

**1939:** Owen purchases the Chicago Terminal National Bank, a small bank west of the Chicago River.

**1940:** Owen and Louise move from Glencoe to 1201 Sheridan Road in Evanston.

**1942:** Owen awarded Alumni Medal by Northwestern University.

**1942-1943:** General Finance purchases six companies involved in war production. They are: Hanlon-Waters of Tulsa, Oklahoma; Climax Engineering Company, of Clinton, Iowa; McAlear Manufacturing Company, of Chicago; Bi-Metallic Products Corporation, of Chicago; Simmons Manufacturing Company, of Ashland, Ohio, and Morrow Manufacturing Company, of Wellston, Ohio.

**1943:** General Finance purchases control of the Wacker Corporation, which owned title to the forty-five-story Civic Opera House at 20 South Wacker Drive in Chicago.

**1944:** The James S. Coon Scholars program is established, benefitting graduates of Rantoul High School who attend Northwestern.

**1945:** Owen purchases a twenty-eight-story building at 184 West Lake Street in Chicago to serve as General Finance's new home.

**1946:** Alice Coon, through a conservator, sues Owen challenging their 1929 divorce. (The lawsuit was settled with the Coon Estate in 1950.)

**May 22, 1946:** The Owen L. Coon Foundation is incorporated in Illinois.

**June 1, 1946:** First meeting of the foundation is held at the Coons's house in Evanston.

**1947:** Owen purchases Intercontinental Engineers and real estate for the foundation.

**August 2, 1948:** Owen dies of leukemia.

**1948-1961:** Paul Morrison serves as president of the foundation.

**March 8, 1954:** The board sets up the Owen L. Coon Foundation Fund at Northwestern University by making an initial $25,000 contribution. The fund would pool foundation money destined for future Northwestern projects.

**1961-1991:** Harry Coon serves as president of the Owen L. Coon Foundation.

**1968:** The board accepts an offer by CNA Financial to pay $32 per share for General Finance Corporation stock owned by foundation. The foundation owned 111,000 shares, worth $3.55 million.

**November 17, 1970:** The board votes to end yearly funding of the Hardy Scholarships program, but it continues to operate.

**1991-present:** Richard O. Briggs serves as president of the Owen L. Coon Foundation.

# Principal Grants of Owen L. Coon Foundation, 1946 - 2006

---

**To Northwestern University:**

Clarion DeWitt Hardy Scholarships, School of Speech (now School of Communication), 1946 - Present.

Clarion DeWitt Hardy Scholarships, School of Law, 1947 - 1973.

Owen L. Coon Debate Tournament, 1958 - Present.

Construction of Owen L. Coon Law Library, 1959.

Owen L. Coon Foundation Fellowships in Medicine, 1971 - 1987.

Construction of Owen L. Coon Forum, 1974.

Owen L. Coon Chair in Law, 1974.

Owen L. Coon Chair in Psychiatry (now Psychiatry and Behavioral Sciences), 1974.

Construction of Owen L. Coon Laser Laboratory, 1979.

Owen L. Coon Professorship in Molecular Biology, 1987.

Owen L. Coon Endowed Scholarship Fund, 1993 - Present.

James A. Rahl/Owen L. Coon Senior Research Program, School of Law, 1997- Present.

James S. Coon Scholarship Fund, established in 1944 by Owen Coon, supplemented by foundation 1998-2001.

Owen L. Coon Fund for Public Debate, 1998.

Owen L. Coon Professorship in Argumentation and Debate, School of Communication, 2001.

**To Evanston Hospital (now Evanston Northwestern Healthcare):**
Louise W. Coon Chair of Medicine, 1970.

Construction of Owen L. Coon Cardiac Catheterization Laboratory, 1978.

Construction of Owen L. Coon Ocular Diagnostic and Treatment Center, 1981.

Construction of Owen L. Coon Research Center, 1987.

Owen L. Coon Chair in Cardiothoracic Surgery, 2003.

# Hardy Scholars

## School of Speech*
### 1935-36
William F. Babcock
John E. Fobes
Horace W. Howells
Page S. Procter Jr.
James A. Rahl
Gloria K. Rensch
Lewis H. Sarett Jr.
Paul F. Schwaighart Jr.

### 1936-1937
Harold O. Davidson
Robert E. Waggoner

### 1937-1938
Ernest L. Badenoch
Albert W. Boulton
Dwight W. Croessmann
Peggy Dunn
Hugh K. Jennings
Howard C. Long
William M. McCandless
J. Austin Ranney
Fred D. Shandorf Jr.
Herbert R. Silvers
J. Richard Swenson

### 1938-1939
Roy E. Henry
Robert J. Salvesen

### 1939-1940
Harald Christopher
Betty Lea Evans
Jack E. McCandless
Jules Power
S. Jay Savereid Jr.
Elizabeth Simmons
William M. Siegel

### 1940-1941
Georgia Bayless
Don J. Geiger
Catherine Hopfinger
Paul A. Larson
James J. Rathbun

### 1941-1942
Georg M. Babbe
John H. Caster
John P. Forester
Lloyd J. Klein
Wilson L. Nicoll
Mary Ellen Robinson
Mary Louise Sauer

### 1942-43
William F. Bell
Duane P. Benson
Warren N. Eggleston
Robert Thedens
Raymond S. Woodard

*(now Communication)

**1943-1944**
Carolyn Anne Bennorth
William C. Lantz

**1944-1945**
Jack E. Brown
Joyce Dix
Eunice Uebele
Eugene L. Wyman

**1945-1946**
Edith Bannon
E. Allan Kovar

**1946-1947**
Robert Carson
Charles P. Sohner
John Snider
James H. McBath
Betty Clark
A. Arthur Davis

**1947-1948**
George N. Greene
Gordon Linkon
James H. Werner

**1948-1949**
John A. Grayson
Dean A. Olds
Sander Vanocur

**1949-1950**
Otto F. Bauer
Richard M. Markus
Richard P. Mathison

**1950-1951**
Milton James Brown
Morris J. Niedenthal
Thomas J. Simmons
Robert A. Southern

**1951-1952**
Richard C. King
John L. McClaugherty

**1952-1953**
Frederic A. Neyhart
James R. Mitchell
Max Nathan Jr.
Albert M. Sconberg

**1953-1954**
Harold J. Borden
Marvin S. Martin
Stephan A. Thernstrom

**1954-1955**
Louis H. Beres
John W. Spalding
Harry V. Wappler

**1955-1956**
Anthony J. Mulac

**1956-1957**
Thomas W. Brunner
Eldon W. Lanning
John. C. Lehman
Jack J. Rorem
Clinton D. Tompkins

**1957-1958**
Dale W. Hagen
Richard D. Kirshberg
Donald R. Steinle

**1958-1959**
David M. Ebel
Bruce W. Lyon
Edwin A. Musselwhite
Reinette E. Newbold
Michael S. Strah

**1959-1960** (No new names)

**1960-1961**
Robert S. Hoberg
James F. Smith
William T. Smith

**1961-1962**
Jerome E. Egel
Gary L. Goodman
John E. Olson
Gene P. Schultz
John D. Strickler
Paul Gary Werskey

**1962-1963**
H. Russel Barefield
Phillip S. Fry
Allan Goodman
C. Wesley Morriston
Fred. T. Plog III
David N. Smith
William E. Snyder

**1963-1964**
Gregory W. Campbell
Robert H. Chandler
Michael L. Denger
John M. Holcomb
William B. McClure
Raymond E. Venghaus

**1964-1965**
Martin R. Galbut
Thomas A. Harris
Garry G. Mathiason
Stephen E. Morgan
John F. Ritter

**1965-1966**
Bjarnie R. Anderson
Michael L. Blim

Robert L. Garrison
David Zarefsky

**1966-1967**
Richard M. Bernard
John R. Jordan
Michael H. Morris
Gordon M. Patterson
Raymond D. Pike
Curtis L. Sytsma
Ronald J. Waicukauski

**1967-1968**
Steven E. Gunderson
Dan C. Hinds
Frank C. Morris Jr.
Kevin J. Sherman

**1968-1969**
Lawrence P. Bemis
David H. Brown
Steven Goldstein
Robert P. Umland
Harry R. Welsh

**1969-1970**
Colin F. Campbell
Gary R. Lewis
Howard Steven Schiffred
Mark S. Utley

**1970-1971**
Paul D. Clote
Ronald L. Marmer
Elliott Mincberg
Danny M. Mueller

**1971-1972**
Henry M. Abelman
Erwin Chemerinsky
Marc J. Strauss

## 1972-1973
William F. Brosend
James P. Davis
David Heller
Richard B. Horrow
A. S. Loewinsohn
Rodney S. Merwin

## 1973-1974
Howard J. Kirschbaum
Louis E. Kaplow
Douglas C. Straus

## 1974-1975
John E. Harris
Bryan E. Bagdady
David B. Love
Kenneth S. Marks

## 1975-1976
Bradley J. Berg
W. Mark Cotham
Phillip Gibson
Gary G. May
Chistopher T. Wonnell

## 1976-1977
Thomas M. Fulkerson
James M. Pfau
Matthew D. Powers

## 1977-1978
John W. Beeder
Martin D. Katz
Philip T. Roberts
Susan G. Winkler

## 1978-1979
John P. Ratnaswamy
Daniel Wolf
Margaret Evans Muller

## 1979-1980
John J. Bradley
David M. Weisberger
Corrine E. Dauber

## 1980-1981
Neil R. Anapol
Christopher Celetino
David S. Cunningham
Lawrence Plunkett
Lance E. Rosenzweig
Paul C. Whitmore
Mark H. Wright
Richard S. Zeilenga

## 1981-1982
Andrea M. Alterman
Virginia Bannigan
Kenneth J. Chesebro
Richard P. Ferrin
Barry L. Johnson
Quentin H. Sigel
William B. Sullivan

## 1982-1983
Gregory S. Antollino
Kevin H. Breunig
Timothy J. Chorvat
Roselyn F. Coyne
Robert E. Easton
Scott N. Gelfand
Gary D. Gerstner
Hayes F. Michel

## 1983-1984
Ian J. Davis Jr.
Thomas M. Krasnewich
Jeffrey E. Kwatinetz
Catherine Palczewski
Rebecca J. Yane

## 1984-1985
Julie A. Arthur
Bernardo A. Attias
Roselyn F. Coyne
Lyn J. Davies
Mindy A. Kaplan
James P. Lamoureux
Leslie A. Lynn
Quentin H. Sigel

## 1985-1986 (No new names)

## 1986-1987
Terence P. Check
Joel A. Christie
Angela K. Conway
Alan Dalinka
J. Scott Maberry
Gordon R. Mitchell
Dan Reiter
Audrey K. Skwierawski
Henry M. Vogel

## 1987-1988
Timothy J. Alderete
Lisa D. Ekman
Mark A. Levenson
Sean R. Townsend
Bradley T. Winter

## 1988-1989
Michael J. Hauswirth
Russel Keller
Michael A. MacFarland
Cameron M. Murray

## 1989-1990
Kimberly J. Morgan
Elizabeth C. Murphy
Russ W. Rosenzweig
Heather R. Smith
Sara E. Schneckloth

Daniel P. Sturgis

## 1990-1991
Jitin Agarwal
Bridget Brocken
Shannon M. Brogan
Andrew Glickman
William K. McNary
Mark D. Price
Ali M. Nizamuddin
Trevor H. Peterson
Nathan M. Smith
Erik T. Verhoef
Daniel E. Wenner

## 1991-1992
Asheesh K. Agarwal
Ronald H. Cornell
Ross E. Kimbarovsky
Ravi Nagubadi
Brian Pelkowski
Donald F. Peterlin Jr.
Matthew D. Strada
Jill M. Webb

## 1992-1993
Roberto Anguizola
Sinan K. Aral
Robin M. Bowler
Nishea V. Clark
Christopher A. Cotropia
Brian T. Fletcher
John B. Frazier
David Hewlwich
Brian H. Lai
Sean J. McCaffity
Mason Miller
Markio Mulligan
Andrew G. Nowell
August H. Schupp
Joseph Terry
Laura L. Veldkamp

## 1993-1994
Arnab K.Chatterjee
Sean M. Gifford
James B. Griffin
Craig D. Hines
Da-Wai Hu
Steven C. Rowley
Ian M. Smith

## 1994-1995
John M. Busby
Charles B. Fletcher
Terrence J. Johnson
Jonathan E. Wells

## 1995-1996
Heather E. Dowling
Michael J. Gottlieb
Lauren E. Kaplan
Leslie Mueller
David M. Nemecek
Todd C. Plutsky
Shuman Sohrn
Megan M. Wood

## 1996-1997
Matthew D. Anderson
Jennifer E. Northam
Shorge K. Sato
Ryan R. Sparacino

## 1997-1998
Jonathan Trace Johnson
Leslie J. Johnson
Adrianna D. Kastanek
Eli J. Kay-Oliphant
Douglas A. Redden
Robert Mcdonagh Smith

## 1998-1999 (No new names)

## 1999-2000
Raja S. Gaddipati
Geoffrey S. Garen
Paul H. Flaig
Noah D. Oliphant
Jonathan D. Paul

## 2000-2001
Jayson D. Leek
Michael J. McGillen
Gregory J. Philips
Latonya K. Starks
Alexandra N. Switzer
Joel M. Wallace

## 2001-2002
Randall Bush
James T. Lux
Jacqueline A. Swiatek

## 2002-2003
Tracy M. Carson
Luke P. Hill
Wardell K. Minor
Jonathan Reynolds
Nick Sethi

## 2003-2004
Avery Dale
Anthony Jardina
Michael Tristan Morales

## 2004-2005
Charles Boynton
Noah Chestnut
Rachel Haig
Mark Hammervold
Serena Raheja
Ravi Shankar
Evan Shive

**2005-2006**
Zach Brown
Rob Mulholland
Sasha Tuzel
John Warden

## Hardy Scholars
## School of Law*
**1950-1951**
R. James Gormley
Joseph Lederleitner
Daniel Walker
Ferdinand J. Zeni Jr.

**1951-1952**
Carl S. Hawkins
Wendell W. Wright

**1952-1953**
Arthur A. Davis
Donald H. Reuben

**1953-1954**
John Bodner
John E. Coons
Richard L. Johnston
Gordon Linkon
Earl E. Pollock
C. Gayden Wren

**1954-1955**
George Kelm
Robert A. Southern
Aaron S. Wolff

**1955-1956**
H. Robert Halper
John W. McNulty
Donald H. Powers

**1956-1957**
Wence F. Cerne Jr.
Donald A. Gillies
Claude R. Sowle
William S. Tennant
Lester G. Zaczek

**1957-1958**
Roger W. Eichmeier
James R. Mitchell
Richard E. Powell
William E. Steude

**1958-1959**
George M. Hollander
Irwin Mushkin
Stuart Nagel

**1959-1960**
Ronald L. Carlson
Francis A. Heroux
John T. Weise

**1960-1961**
Richard N. Flint
Charles B. Marshall
Michael I. Miller

**1961-1962**
William M. Barvick
Richard M. Hirsch
Stephen J. Mrkvicka
Berton S. Sheppard

**1962-1963**
David L. Aufderstrasse
Thomas Brunner
G. Daniel Carney
Alan G. Kimbrell

*(Dates denote year of graduation.)

**1963-1964**
Gerald M. Caplan
Lester A. Jensen
William H. Oswald
Donald B. Pedersen

**1964-1965**
W. Kent Brandon
Craig W. Christensen
Gary M. Crane
Howard Friedman
Francis O. Spalding

**1965-1966**
George W. Dahnke
Kenneth G. Hance
Michael Lew
Jack C. Morse

**1966-1967**
George Fahlgren
Howard Pizer
Sheldon Zabel
Sherwin Zeitlin

**1967-1968**
Charles House
Henry Lawrie Jr.
Harry Pearce
William Pfeiffer
Harry Youtt

**1968-1969**
Brian Butler
Stephen Siciliano

**1969-1970**
Michael Kearns
William Snyder
Theodore Zimmer

**1970-1971**
Robert G. Foster
William H. Theis
Marvin D. Truhe

**1971-1972**
Louis C. Keiler Jr.
William P. Pearce

**1972-1973**
Jeannette P. Meier
John W. Stamper
Richard L. Whitman

**1973-1974**
Robert H. Chandler
David J. Goss
Emil Lippe Jr.
William P. Wilen

Not all individuals listed received Hardy Scholarships during all of their law school years. The following received scholarships but are not graduates of Northwestern University School of Law: Ralph A. McGee, 1951-52; Wilbur Schroeder, 1952-1953; Richard G. Rademacher, 1959-60; Frank T. Sobol, 1961-1962; William Appler, 1963-1964; David Boies, 1963-1964, and Daniel Orth, 1963-1964.

# Owen L. Coon Endowed Scholarship Fund Recipients

**1993-94 Scholars**
Kathleen Lavin

**1994-95 Scholars**
Matthew Himley
Andrew Klump
Amy Koch
Steven Michel

**1995-96 Scholars**
Eva Frankiewicz
Dahlia Hassani
Peggy Hu
Cyrus Lee

**1996-97 Scholars**
Jessica Bluett
Christina Gilmore
Lara Leniton
Michelle Naffziger

**1997-98 Scholars**
Parthapratim Chanda
Rajiv A. Dalal
Lara Leniton
Michelle Naffziger
Brigit Riley
Cecilia Saffold
Joel M. Spenner

**1998-99 Scholars**
Rajiv A. Dalal
Patricia A. Lee
Lara Leniton
David Y. Lo
Joel M. Spenner
Margaret Wong
Kathy Zebracki

**1999-00 Scholars**
Sharon S. Bautista
Ann Kochuveli
Kerry Kolodziej
Blair H. D. Lamb
Tracy A. Motz
Michelle Santiago
Ellen W. Wu

**2000-01 Scholars**
Sharon S. Bautista
Andrianna Kastanek
Kerry Kolodziej
Tracy A. Motz
Kristen A. Milton
Sriranjani Parthasarathy
Michelle Santiago
Maria Steingoltz

## 2001-02 Scholars
Jada Black
Anne M. Dodds
Jennifer K. Fogarty
Jennifer Kerner
Joseph Chang Rock Kim
Ann M. Kochuvelli
Kerry Kolodziej
Tracy A. Motz
Kirsten A. Milton
Victoria E. Moran

## 2002-03 Scholars
Kenley Barrett
Jennifer Carpenter
Katherina Dodelzon
Neha Goel
Rebecca Krasno
Theresa Strukl
Randall Tosch

## 2003-04 Scholars
Kenley Barrett
Katerina Dodelzon
Neha Goel
Theresa Strukl
Randall Tosch
Jessica Young

## 2004-05 Scholars
Keona Childs
Elizabeth J. Kin
Kathryn Schumaker
Lindsay Shapray
Adam Splitek
Roseann Wu

## 2005-06 Scholars
Paul Overmyer
Lindsay Shapray
Chelsea Slaven
Kristina Lois Jean St. Charles
Lauren Strang

# James S. Coon Scholars

---

1960-1961  Richard Korpan

1981-1982  Hyung Lee

1982-1983  Hyung Lee

1983-1984  Hyung Lee

1986-1987  William Gray

1987-1988  William Gray

1988-1989  William Gray

1989-1990  William Gray

1996-1997  Mia Gray

1997-1998  Mia Gray

1998-1999  Mia Gray

# Owen L. Coon Foundation Fellowships In Medicine

---

**1971-72**
Malcolm R. Robertson, MD, renal diseases
Mervyn J. Weis, MD, medicine

**1972-73**
William K. Lee, MD, coronary care
Hock Huat Yeoh, MD, clinical medicine

**1973-74**
Joesph A. Caprini, MD, surgery
Robert M. Craig, MD, medicine

**1974-75**
Aurthur S. Palmer, MD, surgery
Richard L. Phelps, MD, medicine

**1975-76**
Alex J. Bart, MD, anesthesia
Charles Drueck, MD, surgery
James E. Fish, MD, medicine

**1976-77**
Marian F. McNamara, MD, surgery
E. Lee Stock, MD, ophthalmology

**1977-78**
Kathryn M. Edwards, MD, immunology
Richard F. Kehoe, MD, medicine
John J. McGillen, MD, medicine

**1978-79**
Paul C. Land, MD, anesthesia
Edward J. Olinger, MD, medicine

**1979-80**
Sharon L. Dooley, MD obstetrics
Edward J. Olinger, MD, medicine

**1980-81**
Leo I. Gordon, MD, medicine
Allen M. Samarel, MD, medicine

**1981-82**
Linda M. Graham, MD, surgery
Geoffrey M. Zucker, MD, medicine

**1982-83**
Tom C. Krejcie, MD, anesthesia
Jane N. Winter, MD, medicine

**1983-84**
Tat-Kin Tsang, MD, medicine
Marilynn C. Frederiksen, MD, obstetrics

**1984-85**
Kathleen A. Kuhlman, MD

**1985-86**
David Kamp, MD, Pulmonary Medicine
Robert Reff, MD, Psychiatry

# Rahl/Coon Senior Research Program Participants

---

### 2000-01

Kenneth Abell
Eric Bennett
Lisa Blaeser
Paul Brown
John Chi
Patrick Daly
Jay Dickerson
Garrett Dillon
George du Pont
Drew Edwards
Kevin Finnerty
Joshua Grey
Stephen Haedick
Sarah Harris
Jonathan Hauser
Michelle Hayden
Justin Heather
Kurt Hilbert
Anthony Hill
Roman Hoyos
Jennifer Hubbard
Alicia Hunt
Susanne Jennings
Rachel Johnson
Charles Juister
Janice Kang
Marceletta Kerr
Robert Knowles
Hillary Krantz

Claudia Launer-Campos
Todd Lloyd
Alexander Long
Michael Mandell
Deena Margolies
Mark Marino
Heather McClean
Joel McGuire
Mike Obernesser
Alexander Oses
Drew Panahi
Michael Pardon
Morris Patacky
Carla Pope
Sarah Ritch
Christopher Roberts
Jamie Roginski-Kord
Kate Schank
Seth Schwartz
Rebecca Shapiro
Giel Stein
Morse Tan
Carrie Taubman
Kathryn Tongue
Holly Travis
Morgan Ward-Doran
Drew Weinstein
Andrew Young
Matt Young
Dawn Yuster

## 2001-02

Meir Braunstein
Edwin Buxton
Linus Chan
Shannon Charles
Carolyn Frazier
Michelle Gauthier
Cathy Gerlach
Avitai Gold
Richard Hayes
Jeremy Heckman
Anne Hunter
Michelle Jordan
Coleen Kalbacher
Margaret Kaplan
Kathleen Kunkle
Eloise Lawrence
Craig Lee
Kyunghee Lee
Tiana Lee
Aimee Mackay
Sandra Moser
Elizabeth Olson
Jodi Patt
Todd Rusche
Alice Setrini
Julia Sibert
Matthew A. Strickler
Karen Thompson
Roxanne Torabian-Bashardoust
Joycelynn Watkins

## 2002-03

Jeffrey Berger
Jamenda A. Briscoe
Candace Chambliss
Jeffrey Siu-Yuen Chan
Anthony Colangelo
Christoper E. Coleman
Joel Collins
Jonathan Corsico
Tatiana Diez

David J. Feinberg
Joseph Frost
Jaimica Jarvill
Joo Hui Kim
John F. Kness
Grace S. Lee
Sarah A. Lively
M. Kristy Mace
Anna Marks
David M. Marquez
Andrew Mathews
Francis Gant McCloud
Edward McKenna
Ari D. Mintzer
Peter Moore
James Mutrie
Kristine Neal
Laurence Nee
Richard Alexander Nelson
Jeff Oldham
April Perry
Sarah Prepas
Sarah Ralph
Heath J. Rosenthal
Katherine Rowles
Bredale Rucker
Sanya Sarich
Jacques L. Schillaci
Christian Scott
Mark A. Semisch
Blair Jamal Shaw
Nathaniel Spencer-Mork
Matthew A. Strickler
Chuan Sun
Yuji Sun
Arek Sycz
Rebecca Trent
Marcel Valenta
Jill Vizas
Joycelynn Watkins
Christopher White
Daniel I. Yeh

## 2003-04

Amanda Adrian
Kathryn Bennett
Jeanne Caruso
Alison Chin
Jason Christopher
Steven Cohn
Leonard Conapinski
David Cook
Craig Cooley
Nicole DeBruin
Antje Doether
Ada Dolph
Peter Domer
Michael Feinberg
Harris Fischman
Tyree Givens
C. Sebastian GomezAbero
Sarah Goodstine
Melissa Goodwin
Jennifer Hill
W. Clifton Holmes
Melissa James
Daniel Jauchen
Lisa Johnstone
Gail Kim
David Charles Lee
Pei-hsun Ma
Hugh McCullough
Allison McGowen
Corey McLendon
Anita Ortiz
Tiffani D. Smith Peaches
Michael Perl
Christopher Pudelski
John Ridgeway
Carrie Rief
Christopher Roberts
Renai Rodney
Ethan Kirk Ross
Gary Ross
David Sayyed

Matthew Scherb
Scott Schneider
Robin Sinder
Chuan Sun
Emily Taylor
Josh Tepfer
Courtney VanLonkhuyzen
Jacinda Washington
Anthony Zeoli

## 2004-05

Mariam Ahmed
Ismail Alsheik
Uma Amuluru
Suzanne Besu
Alexia Brunet
Lisa Chessare
Deanna Dennis
Felicia Draper
Kristina Garza
Gaetan Gerville-Reache
Jonathan Glick
Johana Gomez
Merkys Gomez
Tiffani Grimes
Amy Hanf
Joe Harper
Ethan Hastert
John Hayes
Sarah Hefling
Dylan Hendricks
Hudson Hollister
J. Doyle Horn
Daron Horwitz
Betsy Judelson
Rebecca Kahan
Andrianna Kastanek
Paul Katz
Michael Kennedy
Chiwen Kiew
Gregory Luloff
Corey Mathers

184

Patrick McMullen
Drew Meyer
Hema Patel
Melinda Pignotti
Zvi Rosen
Rachel Rosenthal
Ericka Schnitzer-Reese
Amy Shavell
Alison Shinsato
Martin Sinclair
Michelle Spak
Claire Torchia
Shannon Torgerson
Paul Tzur
Kimberly Vertolli-Kirk
James Willams
Ran Yan
Jill Yung
Stephanie Zimdah

Kurt Rohde
Anand Singh
Susan Spies
Negar Tekeei
Edward Whang
Kristina Wilson
William Yoon
Vanessa Zimmer

## 2005-06
Taylor Barada
Heather Benno
Alexander Bilus
Shannon Cade
Elisabeth Carey-Davis
Robert Devlin
Benjamin Feuer
Justin Gray
Justin Grewell
Lucinda Gryzenia
TiShaunda Jamison
Marc Johnson
Katherine Karas
Melissa Koh
James Koutoulas
Nathan Larsen
Cary Martin
Charles Mulaney
Jeney Nurse
Eric Olshan
Jessica Phillips

# Owen L. Coon Foundation Directors 1946-Present

Owen L. Coon, 1946-1948
Louise W. Coon, 1946-1991
Carl L. Anderson, 1946-1948
Paul L. Morrison, 1946-1969
Eleanor Coon Briggs, 1946-Present
Harry H. Coon, 1946-1991
William A. Briggs, 1947-1987
Alma S. Coon, 1947-1991
Byron S. Coon, 1947-1969
Harold H. Anderson, 1948-1984
Ray E. Titus, 1949-1969
Owen L. Coon Jr., 1953-Present
Anne Coon, 1956-1961
Mary Ellen (Briggs) Segall, 1959-1974, 1986-Present
Pauline Dowdell, 1961-1992
Suzanne B. Coon, 1965-1972, 1988-Present
Richard O. Briggs, 1969-Present
Hardin H. Hawes, 1970-1980
Richard S. Oldberg, 1970-1977
William S. Turner, 1970-1974
Trowbridge Callaway III, 1974-2004
Arthur T. Schmehling, 1978-1980
Franklin W. Nitikman, 1984-Present
Owen L. Coon III, 1988-Present
Jean Briggs Latka, 1989-Present
Barbara A. Coon, 1992-Present
Tom Latka, 1994-Present

William J. Segall, 1998-Present
Kimberly W. Segall, 1998-Present
Rose Latka, 2002-Present
Loren A. Hansen, 2005-Present

# Acknowledgments

---

The entire Coon family was remarkably helpful and supportive of my effort to write an honest portrayal of Owen L. Coon. Owen's children—Eleanor Briggs, Harry Coon, and Owen L. Coon Jr.—shared family memories, letters, and photographs. Richard O. Briggs, president of the Owen L. Coon Foundation, guided me to sources and helped me check and recheck facts. He was instrumental in the making of this book. All of Owen's grandchildren, who are determined to understand and fulfill Owen's vision, helped in many ways and made me feel like a member of the Coon family. In addition, I received a great deal of help from Matthew Ter Molen, of Northwestern University, and the staff of the Northwestern University Archives. Patrick M. Quinn, Janet C. Olson, Kevin Leonard, and Allen Streicker answered all of my questions. Editing help was provided by Tom McNamee, Michael Williams, Caleb Burroughs, and Cate Cahan. I would also like to thank Leigh Beinen and Adrienne Drell, who believed in the project from the start.

The typeface in this book was designed by French engraver Nicholas Jensen. Born in 1420, Jenson studied under Johannes Gutenberg and went on to develop the first standardized typeface for printers. Many type-faces popular today, like Times New Roman, are based on his designs.